Prai

Everyday Virtues: Class

When my daughter was little, every .....,
thanked the prince for his kiss and told him she'd be in touch after she finished her degree." I wish I'd had the Autry book! What a wonderful way to introduce and open a conversation on the essential elements of good character. Well done.

—*Kathleen Turner*
Actor and activist

I cried, I clapped, I wondered at how two stories—one from long ago and one from today—could be so alike. I saw myself in one tale and imagined how my eight-year-old grandson would react to another. I could have used these stories with my middle school students to complement the Greek and Roman myths. I'd read, listen, and tell these stories in schools, places of worship, before bedtime, or while I exercise. I'd email them to my friends and colleagues. Thanks to myth-makers Jim and Rick Autry for collecting, sharing, and interpreting them and even adding a few stories of their own.

—*Christie Vilsack, former First Lady of Iowa*
Senior Advisor for International Education
at the US Agency for International Development (USAID)

Everyday Virtues is an amazing collection of stories from all over the world. The collection shows that people, no matter their background or nationality, are faced with the same issues and the same resolve. What a wonderful way to convey life lessons to our children and grandchildren! Even without the explanation at the end of each story, the stories are easily understood at any age. Whether through laughter or tears, each story resonates with the reader and the listener. I look forward to sharing *Everyday Virtues* with family and friends, especially my five grandchildren.

—*Sharman Bridges Smith*
Former State Librarian of Iowa
Retired Executive Director, Mississippi Library Commission

Understanding that children learn very little through admonition but a lot through imagination, the Autrys have given us a fresh and wonderful collection of classic stories from all over the world that teach us how to nurture the "kind-hearted virtues." These tales for children—for all of us, really—open the heart. Taken together, they lead us to appreciate how all the virtues are interconnected.

—*Betty Sue Flowers*
Professor Emeritus, University of Texas at Austin
Former Director, Johnson Presidential Library

These stories invite children and adults to read together, to examine the spectrum of human behaviors, to connect to our innate urge to protect and nurture each other. The tales are about six virtues that are antidotes to the daily media messages that tell us to avoid discomfort by consuming. Each tale offers a moment of choice, a chance to take care of the self or to let go of the fear that we will lose our money, our image, even our life and recognize the need in the other. The cumulative effect of these moments is a gradually more open heart, an awareness that compassion connects us. Even the smallest deed matters. The collection offers voices from many times, places, and belief systems, suggesting that conflicts similar to those in the stories will arise for each of us and deserve consideration. Wading into each tale, we feel viscerally what choice we would make and are more prepared to face our real choices. Hearing the voice of a trusted adult read this collection, a child could not help but engage in a dialogue about the heart and what makes us human.

—*Vicki Goldsmith,*
Former Iowa Teacher of the Year
Finalist, National Teacher of the Year

This book of stories by James and Rick Autry is a wonderful way to share life's most important virtues with children. The focus on such virtues as compassion, justice and humility is so important to children's healthy development. Indeed, this book could not have come at a time when our society more needs exactly this—a focus on what makes us human. These stories entertain, educate and challenge us to embrace our best positive selves. I can think of no better way to strengthen bonds with children than to read this wonderful book. I can't wait to share with my three children.

—*Daniel Clay*
Dean, University of Iowa College of Education

Everyday VIRTUES

Classic Tales to Read with Kids

BY JAMES A. AUTRY & RICK AUTRY

ILLUSTRATIONS BY MICKEY CARLSON

Smyth & Helwys Publishing, Inc.
6316 Peake Road
Macon, Georgia 31210-3960
1-800-747-3016

Library of Congress Cataloging-in-Publication Data on file.

Names: Autry, James A., author. | Autry, Rick, author. | Carlson, Mickey,
illustrator.
Title: Everyday virtues : classic tales to read with kids / by James A. Autry
and Rick Autry ; illustrations by Mickey Carlson.
Description: Macon, GA : Smyth & Helwys Publishing, [2017] | Includes
bibliographical references. | Summary: A collection of twenty-four stories
in different genres, selected to illustrated the virtues of justice,
humility, courage, compassion, freedom, and respect. A lesson and notes on
the story's origin follow each selection.
Identifiers: LCCN 2017033021 | ISBN 9781573129718 (pbk. : alk. paper)
Subjects: LCSH: Virtues--Juvenile fiction. | Short stories, American. | CYAC:
Virtues--Fiction. | Conduct of life--Fiction. | Short stories.
Classification: LCC PZ7.1.A973 Eve 2017 | DDC [E]--dc23
LC record available at https://lccn.loc.gov/2017033021

ALSO BY JAMES AUTRY

Books

Choosing Gratitude: Learning to Love the Life You Have
Choosing Gratitude 365 Days a Year (with Sally Pederson)
Looking Around for God: The Oddly Reverent Observations of an
Unconventional Christian
The Book of Hard Choices (with Peter Roy)
The Servant Leader: How to Build a Creative Team, Develop Great
Morale, and Improve Bottom-line Performance
The Spirit of Retirement
Real Power: Business Lessons from the Tao Te Ching
(with Stephen Mitchell)
Confessions of an Accidental Businessman
Life & Work: A Manager's Search for Meaning
Love & Profit: The Art of Caring Leadership

Poetry

Nights under a Tin Roof: Recollections of a Southern Boyhood
Life after Mississippi
On Paying Attention: New and Selected Poems

Videos

Love & Profit
Life & Work
The Spirit of Work

ALSO BY RICK AUTRY

Word Origins for Lawyers (American Bar Association)

DEDICATION

To my wife, Sally, who has done so much
for people with disabilities. —JAA

To my family, including my future grandchildren. —RA

And we especially dedicate this book to all the teachers,
librarians, grandparents, parents, and friends who care
enough about kids to read to them and encourage
them to read to themselves. —The Authors

ACKNOWLEDGMENTS

I would be remiss if I did not make special mention of my son Rick, who agreed to co-author this book and who, in fact, ended up doing the major research and writing. He ends up far more the author than I.

I must acknowledge my wife, Sally Pederson, who, in watching me worry my way through one book after another, exhibits patience and encouragement through it all.

I am grateful also to Keith Gammons of Smyth & Helwys for his confidence. And I owe a big thank-you to Leslie Andres, who brought much-needed good will and support, as well as a keen eye, in her role as editor.

Finally, I give tribute to Mickey Carlson, artist and friend, whose drawings add a great measure of elegance and sophistication to the book.

—JAA

I must acknowledge the considerable efforts of my dad, who single-handedly kept this book alive for twenty years and did everything he could to make it a reality.

I also am grateful for the charming illustrations of Mickey Carlson. By enhancing our stories so well, they provided that push of inspiration when it was most needed.

Finally, I must thank my wife, Lyn, who listened to me tell stories night after night and helped me to find the right ones.

—RA

CONTENTS

PREFACE

by Jim Autry

To parents, grandparents, uncles, aunts, teachers, and any other adults who may be reading these stories with kids: the stories in this book have been selected because they illustrate what Rick and I call "the kind-hearted virtues," the virtues that all of us must make a part of our very fiber every day if we are to be truly human and if we are to participate fully in our communities and in our world.

And how better to teach these virtues than through the oldest and most enduring teaching tools known to human-kind: stories. Though our world has developed many technical means to tell stories, there is no better way to reach the imaginations of children and young people than through the voice of a respected and beloved adult. And, frankly, there's no better way for that adult to connect with the child than by reading a story.

The tales in this book have been carefully gleaned from an extensive review of children's stories and folk tales. Some of the stories are well known, while others are more offbeat.

The basic criterion for selection, in addition to the educational one, was that the story be striking and memorable. Although the stories come from many traditions, there was no conscious attempt to be artificially representative of the world's cultures. In addition to using stories from the storytelling traditions, this book tells stories based on the lives of famous people or incidents in history.

The objective of this collection is to act as a reference point for adults and children to discuss the importance of the kind-hearted virtues and how we can realize them in our lives every day. Many of these virtues are so complex that youngsters can understand them only in concrete settings. For example, Justice is one of the concerns of those who care about how others are treated, but if it is not tempered by other concerns, Justice can degenerate into revenge. It's not an easy concept to grasp.

The stories herein allow parents and children to consider how the virtues were made real in particular settings and to use their lessons as a guide for everyday living.

The everyday virtues we have chosen to feature are justice, courage, humility, compassion, freedom, and respect.

As a special aid to parents and other readers, we have included two special commentaries, "Story Notes" that explain the history and background of each story and "Lessons of the Heart," a brief discussion of how each virtue fits into the pantheon of virtues. As you will see, they often interlock in ways that make separation seem almost arbitrary. Yet that is part of the point. In striving toward a good life, a person must work to balance these virtues and assure that they constantly inform and work with one another.

INTRODUCTION

by Rick Autry

Here is a book long in making and much in need. The idea for the book came many years ago, back when we were told of family values being in decay, and how the antidote was instructive literature for children. My sons were young at the time, so I had tried some of this literature, but I was never satisfied. The things I sought to teach, the important things, the big things that last a lifetime, were neglected. So I made do with what stories I knew, and could find, and could make up. And slowly I found some traditional stories that I could use. I told my father about them—Dad, who is also a storyteller—and we started to write a book. Back before the Internet and blogs and hyperlinked cross-references, we slowly compiled timeless stories, forgotten stories, stories of substance and durability. Slowly, we wrote.

But sometimes children grow faster than books. And before we had a book, even half a book, the time had passed. My boys grew up, and children's books were set aside. Yet the years flowed on, as years have a tendency to do, until the moment arrived once more. Cruelty and arrogance and disrespect have come to be perversely admired. Dad and I turned to each other, and we decided that the world could use some gentle virtues. And so we contacted a publisher and searched again for stories.

The stories we sought had to have two things. They had to illustrate the gentle virtues that are lifelong and unforgettable. And they had to be good stories.

My idea of what to teach children was influenced long ago by Natalia Ginzburg's essay "The Little Virtues." Her premise is that children "should be taught not the little virtues but the great ones. Not thrift but generosity and an indifference to money; not caution but courage and a contempt for danger; not shrewdness but frankness and a love of truth; not tact but love for one's neighbor and self-denial; not a desire for success but a desire to be and to know." There is nothing wrong with the little virtues. They still need to be taught, and practiced when needed. They are, after all, virtues. The problem is the failure to appreciate that the little virtues are small; it is the failure to understand forces that emphasize such virtues and seek to make us live by them, content in the smallness. In modern America, the little virtues tend to be virtues of the economic system that emphasize gain and consumption. Thrift, industry, caution, and even loyalty all have a function that serves to keep those in power satisfied. Our book does not avoid these virtues because they are wrong but because we seek to teach virtues that benefit the child first. Think of the people you remember from years ago, the people who stand out in your life. No one ever says to someone, "Hey, remember Beth Ann? What a great person! She was so thrifty!" We remember the generous, the kind, the bold. Children who will grow to be remembered as extraordinary should learn such virtues. So we tried to choose not virtues that serve the economy but that build community, not institutional virtues but personal ones, not virtues of the pocketbook but of the heart.

Advocating a virtue, any virtue, does no good if the lesson is not learned. And there is no better way to teach lessons than through stories. It is said that people need heroes. Our need is more than that. Every hero has a story. What we need is the story. When I studied philosophy, I learned from Aristotle that "Man is a rational animal." When I studied anthropology, they taught us another observation by Aristotle: "Man is the social animal." When these combine, we have the basic insight that humans are storytelling animals. We are social; we must talk to each other. We tell each other stories. We entertain by the story, by the suspense of "what will happen next?" And the story makes sense of the world. It satisfies our need to have a rational world, a world that we can understand as somehow fundamentally human. This need for stories can be both a strength and a weakness. If we face some problem that doesn't fit into a narrative but is based on trends and charts and statistics, then more often than not the problem goes unnoticed by the public. What the problem needs in order to get attention is a hero with a story. Only then can it make sense to us at a human level.

We understand best from stories. And a good story, one that not only satisfies but also instructs, is a treasure. It is a treasure that will last a lifetime and be handed down beyond a lifetime.

One of my favorite authors is Ray Bradbury. Someone once asked me what he wrote, and I replied, "He writes stories you take twenty minutes to read, and remember for the rest of your life." It is to that sort of story that we aspire. Our stories are no Ray Bradbury collection, but they are well-loved stories from around the world. It is our hope that they will engage and instruct and endure in the way that only stories can. It is the great mystery and miracle of good stories that they are only words on paper, breath in the wind, and yet they never pass away. That reminds me of a story. It is the story "Something from Nothing" from the Jewish tradition.

* * *

A long time ago in far Russia, back when people didn't have bathtubs in their houses, Joseph the Tailor and his wife, Abby, had a happy home and a young daughter named Gilley. Sadly, by the time Joseph's granddaughter was born, his beloved Abby had passed away. So Gilley named her baby "Abigail" after the child's grandmother. Joseph was inspired by this, and he decided he should make something special as a gift from Abby to Abigail. He found an old soft yellow and white dress that Abby had loved to wear. It was soft as a grandmother's kiss, with yellow flowers as bright as a happy day. Joseph decided he could make it into a very special gift.

He took the dress into his workshop, where he snipped and he stitched, stitched and snipped. In and out he stitched, roundabout he snipped. In and out, round about, until out came a blanket. A beautiful soft blanket, soft like a grandmother's kiss and bright as a happy day. Many days young Abigail slept under the blanket, and when she grew old enough she carried the blanket with her everywhere. Day in and day out she carried the blanket. After a time her mother, Gilley, noticed the blanket had grown tattered. She told Abigail it was time to give up her blanket.

"No!" cried young Abigail. "Not my blankie! Grandma blankie!"

Abigail stomped her little feet and pouted at the thought of losing her blankie made from her grandmother's dress. Fortunately, her grandfather Joseph had an idea.

He took the blanket into his workshop. He snipped off the tattered bits and folded them under. Then he snipped and he stitched, stitched and snipped. In and out he stitched, roundabout he snipped. In and out, round about, until out came a beautiful scarf. The scarf was soft as a grandmother's kiss, as bright as a happy day. And Abigail loved it as much as she had loved her "Grandma blankie."

Abigail wore her "Grandma scarf" all the time, every day. In the winter she wore it inside her coat. In the summer she wore it over her gown. And as the years passed the Grandma scarf too became tattered and worn. Again Gilley suggested it was time to set aside the scarf.

"But Momma," argued Abigail, "this scarf is from Grandma Abby's dress. I am named for her, and I never met her, and this is how I wrap her around my neck like a hug."

Still Gilley knew that the scarf was too shabby to wear anymore. Fortunately, Grandpa Joseph had another idea.

He took the scarf into his workshop. He snipped off the tattered bits, and when he was done there wasn't very much left. But he snipped and he stitched, stitched and snipped. In and out he stitched, roundabout he snipped. In and out, round about, until out came a beautiful hair bow. The bow was as soft as . . . well you know how soft and bright it was. And you know that Abigail loved it, as she loved anything that came from the grandmother she was named for.

Abigail wore her "Grandma bow" all the time, every day. She wore it proudly in the sunshine. And in the rain she wore it under her rain hat. And in the winter she wore it under her stocking cap. Whatever the weather, she was happy to wear her Grandma bow, like a bright happy day in her hair, like a soft kiss on the top of her head.

One day when Abigail came home, her mother noticed something was missing.

"Abigail," asked Gilley, "where is the Grandma bow?"

Somehow the bow had fallen out of Abigail's hair. She panicked.

"Momma! Grandpa Joseph! We have to find my Grandma bow! We have to!" urged the teenage girl who had been named for her grandmother.

They looked and looked. They looked everywhere. They looked anywhere they could imagine, and they looked in places they could not imagine. But never did they find the bow. Abigail was heartbroken.

"Grandpa Joseph, you can fix it, can't you? Momma, tell me Grandpa Joseph can fix it! He can do anything with scissors and thread. He can stitch and snip until I have something of my Grandma's dress. Please tell Grandpa to sew me a happy day and to stitch me my Grandma's kiss."

But Gilley said she could not tell Grandpa Joseph this. She explained that even Grandpa Joseph had to have material to work with.

"I am sorry, Abigail, but even Grandpa Joseph can't make something from nothing."

Abigail cried all through supper. Then, after supper, Grandpa Joseph had another idea. But this time he did not go into his workshop. This time he came and sat on young Abigail's bed as she was crying over her lost bow.

"It is true," he said, "that I cannot sew something out of nothing, but I already have given you something you can keep forever as a gift from me and your grandmother."

"What is that?" cried Abigail.

"You have the story of her dress, and the happiness and kisses it brought to you for all those years. You have the memory of it and the story that it tells. And you too can tell the story, and in the telling remember the happiness, and remember the kisses too. Tell the story anytime you like. Tell it as many times as you like. Tell your children, and your grandchildren, and they too can tell it and remember.

For unlike a dress or a blankie, or a scarf or a bow, a story never wears out and never gets tattered. A story is forever."

So young Abigail dried her tears, and forever after until the end of her days she told this story. A long time ago she was the first person to tell this story. And now you can be the next.

* * *

In this story about stories, Joseph stitched together not just cloth and thread but lives. He was able to stitch together two of the women he loved, who had never met. They were joined by his love of them and by the story they would share. A story, like love, never wears out. We hope that in this collection of stories, your family may find at least one enduring tale that you will love and deem worthy to be handed down.

JUSTICE

There's no such thing as a little bit of justice. We either treat people with justice or we don't. Sometimes it's a difficult balancing act, particularly when considering the virtue of compassion.

Unguided by justice, compassion can lead us to give support to people who should be resisted or fought. Indiscriminate compassion, such as giving aid to dangerous or destructive people out of concern for them as fellow human beings, can lead to even more suffering. This is not only about how our justice system should work but also about how we personally should live by the everyday virtues, considering each injustice an outrage and celebrating whenever justice is done.

The people learn that justice requires wisdom and fairness.

THE STOLEN SMELL

what happens when someone tries to push justice too far

I do not really say that this story is true, but someone once told it to me, and now I will tell it to you.

Once in a great city of a far-off land, on the coast of a sky-blue sea, lived a poor man named Evren [EHV-ren]. Evren was so poor that the only thing he had to eat was bread, and he could not even buy anything to put on his bread. No mustard, no butter, no jam. No flavor at all— just the plain, dry bread.

One day Evren stood in the marketplace of his city. He held the loaf of bread that he would eat that day. He had in his pocket only one small coin. It was enough to buy some bread for the next day but not enough to buy anything else. So it looked like bread today and more bread for tomorrow.

Evren thought to himself, "Today, I eat bread. Tomorrow, I will eat bread. Yesterday, I ate bread. On the day before that, all I had was bread. And on the day before that I had only . . . bread."

With this sad thought, Evren looked around at all the fine foods the sellers were offering to people in the market. There were sweet fruits and fresh fish. Baskets filled with figs and dates hung from the ceilings, and steaming pots of rice and wheat bubbled on the stove. Colorful salads and bright desserts were spread out on tables in magnificent displays. He licked his lips just thinking of all these delights that he could not have. Worst of all was the smell. It was hard enough to smell the boiling stews and the new baked cakes, but the smoke coming from the cooking meats was more than he could stand.

Evren stood next to a meat seller who was cooking the best cuts of lamb and goat over a smoky fire flavored with cinnamon and cloves. The meat had been soaked overnight in olive oil with onion juice and bay laurel so that it was juicy, tender, and full of flavor. At least, Evren imagined it was so, because that was all he could afford. His imagination.

Evren could not stand there smelling that meat, knowing he could never have any. So he decided to walk to a part of the market where they sold something beside food and hope that maybe he could find some work. Once he got away from the meat, Evren found he was still hungry. So he took a bite of his bread. He was very surprised when he did.

"Why," he thought, "this bread tastes like the smell from the meat. I must be imagining things."

He took another bite. The taste was faint, but it was there.

"It must be," he thought, "that the smell from the meat has gotten on my bread and now I can taste it."

Then he had an idea. Evren decided that if he went back to the meat seller and held his bread by the chimney where the smoke came out, then at last he would have some flavor on his dinner. And this flavor was free! Or so Evren thought.

He went back to the meat seller's stall and walked by him with a smile. Evren then stood by the grill next to the little chimney that poured out the flavorful smoke. For some long minutes, he held the bread over the smoke, then took a bite of the bread, then held the bread over the smoke and took another bite, and so on. All the time Evren did this, the meat seller watched him, and they smiled at one another. Finally Evren came to the end of his bread. It was with great satisfaction that he popped the last piece into his mouth and chewed.

Once he swallowed, Evren was satisfied. He finally had a little flavor for dinner. He even started to think that his luck would change and maybe soon he would have some money. With a nod to the meat seller and a new sense of hope, Evren started to walk away from the stall. Then the meat seller spoke.

"Wait one minute," the seller said. "You owe me some money."

Evren was confused. "What for?" he asked.

"You owe me money for the flavor you put on your bread."

"How could I possibly owe you anything?" replied Evren. "I held my bread in the smoke. I ate the bread, not the smoke."

"But you enjoyed the flavor of the bread, did you not?"

"Yes," said Evren.

"When you listen to music and enjoy the music, then you pay the musician. You enjoyed the flavor so you must pay me. After all, you got the flavor from the smoke. The smoke got its flavor from my meat. I bought the meat; I prepared the meat and the spices. It was my goods and my labor that made the smoke so full of flavor. And the smoke made the bread taste better. You must pay for that. My meat, my spices, and my skills are not free."

Evren could not believe what he was hearing. "I will not pay," he insisted. "It is smoke, and smoke is in the air, and air is free. You cannot make me pay for what you were pouring into the air without a thought."

As the argument grew louder and louder, people started to gather around. Some people took the meat seller's side, saying, "After all, he had to spend money to make that smoke." But most people took Evren's side, saying, "Air is free; he is right."

Eventually, one of the onlookers called to a woman named Adalet [AH-doh-lay], whose name means "Justice." The people of the market regarded her as a woman of good sense and fair judgment. She was often called upon to judge cases. The people asked Adalet to judge this case between the meat seller and Evren.

"I will judge," she said, "if the two sides will agree to abide by whatever I decide."

Both the meat seller and Evren agreed, for both had heard of the wisdom and fairness of Adalet. Each man pleaded his case. The meat seller argued that while his smoke had been free when no one used it, if they were to use it then they must pay for the privilege. Evren argued that there was no price on the smoke, and that just because he thought of using it does not mean he agreed to pay a price. Each man asked for Adalet to consider and rule for him.

Adalet thought for a few minutes, and then she looked to Evren.

"Do you have any money?" she asked.

Evren's heart sank, for he was sure he must have lost if she was asking for his money.

"Yes," he said, "just this small coin."

Evren showed the coin to Adalet. Adalet took the coin, looked close at it, bit it, and even smelled it to make sure it was real money. Then she spoke.

"I find that indeed Evren has used the smell of the meat, and that something is owed for that use," she said.

Then she took the coin, put it on her thumb, and, making a loud ping, flipped it back to Evren. While the ping was still sounding out, Adalet announced to the meat seller, "For the smell of your meat, he owes you—the sound of his money!"

Everyone who heard the wise ruling of Adalet agreed that she was right, and the story has been told ever since. And Evren's luck really had changed. A man in the crowd decided he liked how well Evren had convinced the judge, so he hired Evren to work for him as a salesman. The next day, Evren ate more than just bread flavored with smoke.

LESSONS OF THE HEART

There is an old saying that "nothing is more unfair than justice taken too far." The meat seller was not entirely wrong. He had paid for the meat and the spices, and his work created the flavor in the smoke. But the meat seller had no way to use the smoke, and he never tried. He had never thought of charging money for smoke until he saw Evren using it. And, of course, no one can own what floats on the wind. Despite all this, the meat seller still decided to try to get money for the smoke. The wisdom of Adalet the Just was that she gave the seller what he deserved—and absolutely nothing more. This is an important part of justice.

Story Notes

This story is found in many lands and in many sources. One source, which cites seven separate sources, is Sharon Creeden's *Fair Is Fair: World Folktales of Justice* (August House, 1994).

THE MAN WHO KILLED HIS GREYHOUND

a Welsh legend that cautions against the dangers of anger and haste

Once, a long time ago in a place called Wales, there was a husband and wife who had wanted a child for many years but had none. As a result, they heaped much of the affection they had stored up for children on their family dog. Then, one year, they were very happy when they finally had a fine baby boy. They were worried that their dog, a greyhound, might be jealous, but instead the animal seemed to love the child as much as they did.

One day, while the baby was still in his cradle, the wife went away to visit her relatives. The husband stayed at home by himself to tend to their child and household. During this time he heard through his open window the cry of hounds chasing a stag. The husband loved to hunt and thought he would go out and watch the hunt finish and also claim the part of the stag that would be his if it were killed on his land. He worried about leaving the child alone, but he thought since he would be right back and the dog was there and the child was in the cradle, no harm could come to the child.

While he was gone, a wolf came about the house. The wolf was hungry because the dogs had chased the game away from the woods. The wolf saw the open window and took a chance that no one was home. He jumped into the house to look for food.

The wolf never dreamed to find a helpless baby still in the cradle, so he stealthily jumped up on the cradle, turning it over. The baby was trapped beneath it and started to cry. Before the wolf could get to the baby, the greyhound fell upon him. Back and forth they fought. The wolf was larger and driven by hunger but also weakened by that same hunger. The greyhound, who could have simply run away, fought as fiercely as ten wolves. They burst the front door open, and finally the greyhound killed the wolf by the side of the house. The greyhound came back in and lay down next to the crib, slept, and tried to heal his wounds. Eventually, the baby fell asleep again under the cradle.

When the man came home, where he should have stayed all along, his greyhound came up to meet him. The man saw that the greyhound was covered in blood. He looked around and found the cradle upturned and a pool of blood on the floor. Immediately he thought that the greyhound, in his jealousy, had killed the man's beloved son. In a fit of rage the man drew out his sword and killed his dog. He then went to the cradle and turned it over. When he did this, he found his child unhurt. When he looked around a bit more, he found the dead wolf and noticed that the blood on the greyhound came from the wounds the wolf had given the dog. When he realized that the greyhound had risked his life to save the baby, he was sorry forever.

LESSONS OF THE HEART

From this man we learn that we are not able to be fair when we act out of anger. Before we seek justice we must understand what has happened, and we must not punish without thinking first. If we act in haste, then surely we will be as sorry as the man who killed his greyhound.

Story Notes

This is an oft-told Welsh legend. I first ran across it in D. Parry-Jones's *Welsh Legends and Fairy Lore*. In *The Penguin Book of World Folk Tales*, it is called "Llewelyn and Gelert," while a similar story is the Panchatantra story "The Loyal Mongoose." Gelert is the dog, and legend has it that he is buried in a grave mound at the village of Beddgelert in northwest Wales. If you ever find yourself in Beddgelert, you can visit the memorial to the eternally loyal dog.

OLLANTAY AND THE INCA'S DAUGHTER

a story of justice from the ancient Incas

In the time of legends, in the time of heroes, in the time when time was young, there lived a people, the Incas, who dwelt in cities they built high in the mountains. They knew many things about art and science. They knew how to build out of stone blocks without using cement. They knew how to build bridges that hung by ropes hundreds of feet in the air. They knew about war. And from Ollantay [OY-yahn-tee] they learned about justice.

Ollantay was a general. He had fought many battles to uphold the laws of his king. He had won. He had always proven to be smart and brave. He was therefore the most famous general in the empire of the Incas. But even so, when he fell in love with Cusy-Coyllur [COO-see COY-your], the daughter of the king, he knew that his life would be changed forever. The king of the Incas was considered to be a god. Under the law, the members of the royal family were far superior to any normal people. A mere man like Ollantay could not marry the daughter of the king. Although Ollantay had fought to uphold the law, he now rebelled. He knew that Cusy-Coyllur loved him, and so he told her of how he loved her.

Since Ollantay and Cusy-Coyllur were in love, they decided that they must get married. But they could not get married in the open. So they told all their friends at the palace about their plans but kept the marriage secret from the king. Many people tried to talk them out of the wedding. To get married would be to break the king's most important law. Ollantay would be killed, surely, if the king knew that he dared to marry the exalted princess. Ollantay did not care. To him it was not right that anyone should keep apart people who loved each other as much as he and Cusy-Coyllur. So despite the law and the warnings of their friends, they got married.

It was not long after they married that Cusy-Coyllur decided to chance telling her father. She loved him and was not happy because she had to lie to him every day. She wanted him to share in her happiness and hoped that he would forgive her and let her get married in the open. Together, Cusy-Coyllur and Ollantay went to see the old king. They told him of their love but not yet of the marriage.

The old king was furious. He sent his daughter away to the temple of the sun, where she would be forced to serve the Sun God. She would be guarded day and night. For Ollantay, there was no punishment too great. The lawmakers had never dreamed that any mere general would dare to place himself on the level of the royal family by even asking to marry a princess. Ollantay was stripped of his rank of general. All his honors and titles were taken from him. He was ordered to stay at the palace until the old king could think of a punishment terrible enough for him. Although he was guarded, it was not very difficult for a cunning soldier like Ollantay to find his chance to escape. He could not bear being separated from his wife, so, when he saw his chance, he escaped from the palace. He then made his way to his old headquarters at a large fortress. He called together his captains.

"I have come to say farewell," he told his men. "I must try to free my wife. If I am killed trying, then so be it. But even if I free her, it will not be safe for us in the land of the Incas. We will go beyond the mountains and live there. You will never see me again."

When he told them this, his captains stood up and swore their loyalty to him. They told him they would follow him wherever he should lead. "We will march at your side," they said. Ollantay had counted on his men to follow him. He knew that with them, he had a real chance of freeing his Cusy-Coyllur and staying with her in their homeland. He would try to change the law and convince the king that his service to the country should count more than the fact that he was not born a prince. Ollantay and his soldiers set out at dawn.

By chance, another general, Ruminahui [room-in-AH-wee], saw Ollantay's army and realized what must be going on. While Ruminahui was a good general, he knew that he would be no match for Ollantay in a battle. Rumi-nahui made a plan to trick Ollantay. He told his troops to follow him but to stay out of sight. He then went by himself to the camp of Ollantay's army. The camp was an old fortress guarded by a high wall. Ruminahui presented himself at the gate, and when he was brought to Ollantay, he said that he had come to help. Ruminahui convinced Ollantay that he also thought the law was unfair and that he could help Ollantay get more soldiers. But in the night, Ruminahui got out of bed quietly and went to the gate. Secretly, he opened the gate and waved to his waiting troops. His army rushed in and surprised Ollantay's sleeping men. In no time, Ruminahui had won the battle and made Ollantay his prisoner. Ruminahui and his men set out for the king's palace with Ollantay in chains between them.

As they traveled to the palace, a messenger met them. The messenger told them of the sad news that he had to bear across the land of the Incas: the old king was dead and his son Tupac Yupanqui [TOO-pawk you-PUN-kee] was now the new king. Ollantay wondered if Tupac would treat him better than his father had. Would he be able to see his wife before he died? Would Tupac have mercy on his sister?

At last they arrived at the palace of the new king. The meeting with Tupac Yupanqui was cold. The new king told Ollantay that he must apply the law. He said that the law was the foundation of the king's strength. If he did not apply the law, he told Ollantay, then others would think he was weak and feel that they could break the law. Ollantay knew this and asked only to be heard by the new king before he died.

"I have always respected and fought for the law," said Ollantay. "I have risked my life for the law many times. But how can you expect the kingdom to be strong if its laws are not founded on justice? Unfair laws will destroy the people's faith in the king faster than no law at all. Is a law just that forbids a man to love a woman, even if he has proven himself a worthy, brave, and faithful servant of the king? Shouldn't I be able to prove myself worthy of royalty by what I have done and not be denied this chance just because I was not born a prince? Know this, great king: your greatness must come not from the strictness with which you enforce your laws but from the justice of them. I submit to punishment." At this Ollantay knelt before the king.

"Stand up," replied Tupac Yupanqui. "I have thought about the questions you have asked about law and justice. Of the two justices, which is the more important? I am going to pardon you and allow you to marry my sister. I hope that you have children and live happily at my court. And let it be known in this kingdom that from now on, a person shall be treated not according to his birth but according to what he has earned."

Just as the king spoke these words, the sun, which had been hidden all day, came out from behind a cloud. It seemed to the king that the sun shone brighter than usual as if to say to him that he had done rightly.

LESSONS OF THE HEART

Justice judges someone by deeds and not by birth. Ollantay had proven himself by his actions, making him worthy of royalty. When the first king refused to recognize this, he made the law an instrument of injustice. But kings, judges, and rules are good or bad based not on how strict they are but on how fair they are.

Story Notes

This is based on a pre-Columbian myth from South America, apparently of Incan origin. Perhaps the earliest written version of the Ollantay story is a play by Antonio Valdes dating to 1770. An early account was widely distributed in 1835, when Manuel Palacios published an academic article about the story. In 1857, Johann Jakob von Tschudi published an early translation of the story into German, titled "Ollanta, ein altperuanisches Drama, aus der Kechuasprache übersetzt und kommentiert."

THE HORSE,
THE BELL,
AND THE KING

*a story of true justice and the proper
reward for a lifetime of devotion*

Over the mountains, over the sea, far from you and even farther from me, there lived a king who ruled the land of Atri. King John of Atri believed a king must care for his people and that the surest way of doing this was to rule the land with justice. So King John decided he would make sure everyone in his kingdom could always call for justice.

King John bought a huge bronze bell and had it hung on a tower in the town square. He had a strong rope tied to the bell, and he had the bell so well-oiled that the slightest tug could move it. He ordered that the rope must hang so low that even the smallest child could reach it.

Then King John had his herald call the people to the square. When they were gathered, King John made his announcement about the Bell of Atri.

"I have placed here the Bell of True Justice. When anyone, anyone at all, feels that they have been wronged, all they need to do is pull on this rope and ring the bell, just so."

King John gave the rope a light tug, and out rang the bell, loud and clear, as pure as the waters of the mountains, as pure as an innocent heart.

"A wrong!" it rang, "a wrong! Justice must be done! A wrong! A wrong!"

King John then explained, "Whenever the bell is rung, and no matter who rings the bell, my judges and I will answer the call as soon as we are able, and we will listen to the claim for justice. If we find a wrong was done, we will order justice for the wrong."

"Can anyone ring the bell?" the people asked.

"Yes, anyone," said King John.

"Even little kids?" asked a little girl and boy together.

"Rich and poor, young or old, girl or boy, man or woman—all of you deserve justice. And no matter who does wrong, that person will have to answer for the wrong," said the king.

The king was as good as his word. For many years, no sooner would the bell ring "A wrong! A wrong! Justice must be done!" than the king and his judges would appear to hear the complaint. They quickly punished those who did wrong, and they made sure that any wrong was corrected and that any loss was repaid. So sure and swift and fair was their justice that after a while the bell was used less and less. This was because whenever people thought to steal or lie or otherwise treat someone unfairly, they thought of that bell and the sure and certain justice that would follow. Doing wrong would never pay when there was the Bell of True Justice to be rung. As time went by, the bell continued to ring less often, and the people became more honest, more generous, more decent and thoughtful and kindhearted.

Over time, through disuse, the long rope on the bell became overgrown with vines. The rope reached down to the ground so that even children could touch it easily, and up from the ground some vines had found the rope. The vines curled around the rope and climbed it, covering it as they stretched toward the sun. As the rope became less used, the vines on it grew thick and lush.

It so happens that at this time in Atri there lived an old knight named Sir Henry who loved money above all things. It was not always so. As a young man, Sir Henry had ridden his horse, his grand charger, across the lands surrounding Atri. The horse had saved his life many times when he had to fight in faraway wars. When there was no war to fight, still Sir Henry would ride through the countryside to look for robbers and keep the peace. If two people were arguing, the knight would take them on his horse to the bell tower so they could call on the king and his judges. The horse had always proudly carried the knight as he rode to his duties. But as all of Atri became more just and more peaceful, the knight was not needed to ride forth quite as much. So he stayed home in his castle. He came to like the comforts of his castle and, above all, to like counting his money. By the time the bell rope was covered in vines, Sir Henry had long since decided that money was more important than anything. He even decided that money was more important than looking after the horse who had served him so well for so long.

By this time, the proud horse had grown old, so that his bones creaked and his joints popped. Still, he was ready to serve the knight any time he was needed. But the knight had no more use for his faithful steed.

"Why should I pay for upkeep of that old nag?" thought Sir Henry. "He does me no good at all. I will send him away and turn him loose."

So the knight set his horse loose, sending him out on the road with no food, saddle, or name, and closed the stable to keep him out. The old horse stood by the gate waiting for the knight to come to him and ask him for a ride. For three long days he waited. And then hunger made him wander off in search of food. For many months the horse wandered across Atri, eating such grass as he could find by the edge of the road, getting older and skinner by the minute. He wandered the long, lonely, shadeless street, barked at by dogs and torn at by thorns. The people of Atri knew the horse and thought to themselves, "What a shame about the old knight's horse." Still, no one else could afford to take in the old fellow, and he was left to wander to look for food through the dark, through the wet, and also under the burning sun.

It came to pass that one day the old faithful horse came into the town square at Atri, and he saw growing up in the middle of the square a long, lush vine covered with tasty leaves.

And then it happened.

"A wrong! A wrong!"

The king was sleeping in his throne room that hot afternoon. It had been a long time since the bell had rung, and now he was not sure he really heard it. He thought maybe it was just a dream. He listened as he sat there. Nothing. He listened some more. Still no sound. Then, as he started to close his eyes again, he thought he heard a faint sound. Just a small tinkle. And then he heard it again, loud and clear.

"A wrong! A wrong! Justice must be done! A wrong! A wrong! Judges, you must come!"

Out came the king, out came his judges, out came the people to see who had called on the forces of justice. As they all came to the square, they saw a skinny, old, worn-out horse eating the lush vines and ringing the bell as he did so. It was obvious to everyone that the horse was not being properly cared for.

King John looked to the people and asked, "Whose horse is this?"

A few of the farmers spoke up. "Why, that is the old horse of Sir Henry, Knight of Atri. He was a proud charger in his day. He served the knight well and saved his life many times. But now Sir Henry loves money more than his horse and refuses to care for him. The horse has no name or owner now, and is seen wandering the public ways eating such scraps as he can find."

"His call for justice has been heard," said the king. "Bring Sir Henry to us for judgment."

After a time, Sir Henry appeared before the king and his judges in the square.

"Is it true that you let this faithful creature go because he no longer serves you? Is it true that you neglect him now that you cannot use him?" asked King John.

"When he served me, I cared for him," replied Sir Henry. "He was paid for his service by my care. I now no longer need his service, so I no longer provide him care. Now he serves himself, and so I leave him to care for himself. Surely a person can do as he wishes with his property?"

King John frowned and replied, "Pride rides forth on horseback grand and gay, but comes walking back on foot. Sir Knight, remember your sworn oath of nobility. What fair renown, what honor, what fame can come to you from starving this poor brute? Faithful service is always to be matched by responsibility to those who depend on us. The end of the service is not the end of the responsibility, for faithfulness goes both ways, and true faithfulness does not end with usefulness. Those like this horse, who serve well and speak not, need justice and care even more than those who make the loudest demands."

Sir Henry hung his head in shame. He had been a noble knight, and he knew that he had done wrong. The horse was faithful to him, and would be to the end. So he must be faithful to the horse. The code of the knight, justice itself, demanded no less.

King John consulted with his judges and then turned to Sir Henry to announce the decision.

"This steed served you in youth," he said, "so from now on you shall make sure to comfort his old age. You shall provide him shelter and food and a field to run in. You shall honor and cherish him in his old age, and plant a special field for him with clover and sweet timothy. For everyone deserves justice, even an animal. So I say, so I award, so I decree!"

Sir Henry, understanding the wrong he had done, bowed his head and said, "So it shall be done."

The people cheered the judgment and shouted, "Hooray for King John. Hooray for the Bell of True Justice."

LESSONS OF THE HEART

The Bell of True Justice must be available to everyone or else it is not true justice at all. True justice is not just a rule telling us what not to do. True justice also commands us to act. While justice requires that people treat each other fairly, true justice is more than making sure people do not take things from one another or harm one another. Justice requires positive action as well. So, for example, true justice demands that those who have served our society but who can no longer care for themselves must be cared for by those they have served.

Anything less and we are no better than Sir Henry when all he cared for was money.

Story Notes

This story appears first in an early Italian collection, *Il Novellino: The Hundred Old Tales,* which dates to around 1300. Five hundred years later, in 1863, Henry Wadsworth Longfellow included it as "The Sicilian's Tale" in *Tales of a Wayside Inn.* The line "Pride goeth forth on horseback grand and gay," etc., was taken from Longfellow.

HUMILITY

One thing you can be sure of: when someone says, "I'm a very humble person," it's not true.

A humble person will not brag about being humble; in fact, bragging is the opposite of humility. Humility is first about who you are and then about what you do. It begins on the inside and then is evident as respect for others.

But humility goes deeper than our relationships with others. We are on the path to humility when we realize that, while all of us are equals as human beings, we are all only human beings. With that comes the further understanding that we can never be perfect. No human being can. We all fall short of what we should be. No matter how hard we work to exemplify all the virtues, if we are truly humble, we will never think we have achieved that perfection.

Thus even the great people of human virtue have been humble. As Confucius himself said, "To have faults and not try to correct them is to have faults indeed."

Humility is the recognition that everyone will always have faults, and if we lack humility we have "faults indeed."

The monks learn to appreciate the most humble of gifts.

THE LITTLE JUGGLER

a story of the value of humble and simple gifts

In the olden times, as they are known, lived Poor Jacques, a wandering minstrel. His only talent was that he could juggle. He was a good juggler but not famous enough to perform with the big circuses. Instead, he made his living by traveling the countryside and juggling for the country folk. His tricks were simple: juggling a few balls, twirling plates on sticks, balancing on a ball while walking, and even some sleight of hand.

It was not easy for Jacques. Many times he performed for a farm family to earn his supper. Almost as many times he went with no supper at all. As the juggler grew older, he grew a little slow and tired. He found it hard to stay alive in the wintertime. Since everyone huddled inside, it was difficult for him to find an audience. As he wandered, hungry, the cold froze him through his rags. Still, he never complained. Whenever he got the slightest reward for his performance, he thought to himself, "I love to juggle. I make my living by doing something that I love to do. God is good. The Virgin will take care of me."

One day as he was saying this thought out loud, he found himself outside a monastery with a large statue of the Virgin Mary in front of it. "Why, this is a house dedicated to the Virgin," he thought. "If only I could stay here, how nice it would be. I could see the Virgin every day and be near her. I could repay her by living the rest of my life in her service. But I don't suppose that I ever could . . . ." Jacques left this thought unfinished as the door to the monastery slowly opened.

A monk stood at the door holding a plate of food. Seeing Jacques standing there so long in his rags, the monk had assumed he was a poor man too ashamed to beg for food.

"Here you go, my good man," said the monk.

"Oh no. It is kind of you, but I have not come to beg for food. Please, I would beg of you something else." The monk looked puzzled while Jacques paused to gather his courage. "You see, I have wandered the countryside my whole life. I have seldom worshiped in a real church. I have often made my own service at roadside altars and in the fields. My heart's desire is that I should repay the Virgin for my good luck by devoting myself to her in a proper place of worship. May I join you and live in the house of the Virgin?"

"Well," said the monk, "we deny no man shelter, but for someone to come and live with us in another matter. Your request is very unusual. What can you do?"

"Not much. I am not learned or very skilled. I am a juggler. I balance things. I can walk on a ball and board. I can keep six or eight balls in the air. I can say my prayers standing on my head. I don't suppose this is the stuff that usually makes a monk. But I can learn. I will do any sort of chore you need done. Tell me what to do—any honest work no matter how dirty or hard—and I will do it gladly if I may show my devotion."

"I cannot make such a decision. I must take this matter to the abbot. Come with me."

The monk took Jacques to the abbot. The abbot was moved by the juggler's sincerity and desire for something different in his life, and he allowed Jacques to join the monastery.

Jacques was as good as his word. He was given the hardest and dirtiest chores of the monastery. In the kitchen, he peeled the turnips and cleaned the pots and pans. He scrubbed the floors on his hands and knees. He took out and emptied the dirty chamber pots in the morning. No job was too hard or humble for Jacques. And yet he was not satisfied. When he first started, he was happy with the chance to show his worth. But as he looked around, he began to feel that he was not doing enough.

He compared the work of the other scholarly monks with his chores. The others were capable of glorious feats in devotion to the Virgin. Some of them composed complex hymns to praise her. Others copied out holy books onto creamy vellum and decorated the pages with intricate designs in the brightest colors. All together, they would sing to her with voices trained for many years.

"All the others do such wonderful deeds to celebrate and delight the Virgin. What have I done for her pleasure?" thought poor Jacques.

Day after day, Jacques worried that he was not doing enough. Even as he went about his chores, he was quiet and withdrawn.

"This I do for her. But it is not enough," he would think.

Still, Jacques had no ideas. His voice was harsh from his years in the hard weather. He had no learning. He had no skill with words or music. He could create nothing, neither sculpture nor carving.

He was a simple juggler, after all. It was a torment to him. But then one night he had a dream. It was a magnificent dream. When he woke, he saw exactly what he should do.

The other monks, who had never paid much attention to Jacques, began to notice a change in him. He was no longer sad and lonely. Before, he would look down when meeting another monk, but now he would hold his head up and greet them with a smile and a cheerful word. Some of the monks noticed that Jacques was always late in returning from Vespers. He would linger long after the others had left. He would stay in the chapel with the doors closed. They started to notice that there were other times when Jacques would stay alone in the chapel. In fact, before long Jacques was spending every spare moment there. He hurried through his work, and as soon as he was free he rushed to the chapel and locked himself in alone.

At first the other monks were pleased to see Jacques becoming comfortable at the monastery. But pretty soon they began to wonder and gossip.

"What could he be doing in there?"

"It is unnatural for someone to be so long by themselves."

"He is not trained as a monk; perhaps he is doing something that isn't right."

Finally, this talk reached the abbot. He called together some of his trusted brethren and put together a plan.

"It would not be proper," said the abbot, "for us to intrude upon Brother Jacques's devotions. Still, it is very odd how he chooses to spend his time, and, as you know, he is new to us. I wonder if after all the time he spent among the common folk, he may have some strange ideas about what to do in a monastery. I think we owe it to the community to clear away any doubt. So that we do not intrude, here is what I suggest: we can open the chapel door just a crack and watch to see what he does. This way we can put our minds at ease and we can all go back to our routine."

The others, who were all curious, agreed with the abbot. So the next time Jacques stayed behind by himself in the chapel, the abbot and his companions were watching from the door. They saw the little juggler standing before a statue of the holy Virgin that stood at the altar. He was performing all the tricks he had performed for the farm and village folk in his travels. He juggled a few balls. He balanced some cups and plates on sticks. He walked on a ball while he juggled plates. He made some things disappear, and he leapt and danced while balancing a broom on his chin.

The abbot could not believe his eyes. The idea of entertaining the Holy Virgin with the simple tricks of a street mountebank! Jacques treated her as if she were some rustic just off the farm! The abbot threw wide the door and strode into the room.

"Sacrilege!" cried the abbot. "Imagine acting the fool in such a holy place. You shall be banned for this!"

The poor juggler was confused and frightened. He was startled by the unseen visitors and ashamed that his gifts were so unworthy. The abbot started towards the juggler, who backed away in fright.

At that moment, the Holy Virgin came down from her altar, smiled, and, to the astonishment of all, wiped the sweat from the little juggler's face.

LESSONS OF THE HEART

Each person lives according to his or her own gifts. As long as we give the best that we are able to give, then no gift, no life, is more precious than another. Thus the Virgin regarded the humble gift of the juggler as highly as any other. Indeed, it was even more valuable because it was given with purity and humility. The juggler gave no thought to impressing others but only to giving the best that he was able.

Story Notes

This is a fourteenth century French legend. A version can be found in *The Penguin Book of World Folk Tales* as "Our Lady's Tumbler" and in the volume *The Firebringer* by Louis Untermeyer. It was famously made into the story "Le Jongleur de Notre Dame" by Anatole France in 1892. It can be found in many versions from Jules Massenet's 1902 opera to a version Andy Griffith told as "Barnaby the Juggler" on his album *The Christmas Guest.*

THE LION WHO SPRANG TO LIFE

an ancient story of respect for the abilities of others

A story, a story, a story I will tell. Of wonders, and marvels, and sorrow that befell.

Far away in the land of India lived four good friends. Three of them had studied sciences, and magic, and secret ways and spells. These three had read many strange and dusty books, and they had gained much wondrous and mysterious knowledge. The fourth friend had spent a life in working, and he had no time for the study of books. This friend, who was named Subuddhi [sue-bu-dye], had instead spent his time toiling among others and listening to what they had to say. His learning came from what he saw and heard all around him. As a result, while they were all friends, the three scholars looked down on Subuddhi, and they pitied him that his knowledge was so incomplete.

"Do not pity me," Subuddhi would say, "for although I am sorry that I have not learned all the secrets you scholars have, I do have good common sense and good judgment. The people in the village all say so."

His friends were not convinced and believed that Subuddhi was only saying this because he was jealous of them.

One day as the four friends sat together, the scholars discussed how they might profit by their knowledge.

"I have studied connections, and bonds above all else," said the first scholar. "I understand how things fit together. My understanding is deep and profound, yet what good does it do me if no one knows of it?"

"That is the same as my problem," said the second scholar, "as I have studied forms and substance. I know what makes things work once they have been connected together. But like you I have no fame, and so my knowledge can earn me nothing."

"So have I studied," said the third scholar, "and yet remain unable to profit by it. My knowledge of movement and drive, of what gives things their energy, is very complete. I am a scholar of the life force itself. But to profit from it, first I must make it known how great I am."

The first two agreed with the third. They wanted above all things to show off their knowledge. Subuddhi only said, "I use my common sense every day, and I live well enough and am content."

His friends smiled at him and said, "Yes, little Subuddhi, that is good enough for you, who have no knowledge of any importance, but we deserve better."

After talking some more, the three scholars hit upon an idea. They decided that they should go through the countryside and work such miracles as they could until people started to notice them. When they became famous, then they could make money selling their knowledge and their miracles.

Subuddhi was content where he was, but he also wished to see more of the world. So he asked his friends if he might come too.

"What good," said the scholar of connections, "would it do us to have this unlearned man along? Wouldn't he just slow us down and make people think less of us for keeping company with a foolish person?"

"Well," said the scholar of form, "he could do chores for us. He could make our fire and cook our food. That way we could focus on important things."

"Friends," said the scholar of the life force, "it is not good for us to be so ungenerous. He is our friend from childhood, and if he wants to tag along we should let him, even if he knows nothing useful and will be a drag on us. We should be friend enough to put up with him."

Subuddhi thanked them for letting him come, and even though they were sometimes rude about his knowledge he was still loyal to his childhood friends.

The next day they started their journey. They walked out of their town and came to a forest. As they walked through the forest, they saw what appeared to be the dead body of a large animal. As they walked past it, the three scholars had an idea.

"I know!" said the first. "Let us bring this animal to life. People who have seen this carcass will recognize what we have done and our fame will start to spread."

"Great idea," said the other two scholars. "This is a wonderful way to show off our knowledge."

"Perhaps," said Subuddhi, "it is better to leave the dead to the care of the dead."

"Such a foolish man," said the others. "You do not study, so you do not understand what we are trying to do. Please stay silent in the face of what is beyond your ability."

Subuddhi stood aside and let them work.

"Now for the connections!" said the first scholar. He waved his hands and chanted his secret spells, and bit by bit he pulled together the skeleton.

Subuddhi could not stay silent.

"My esteemed friends, look at the teeth and the claws on this skeleton. This is an animal that eats other animals. It is better for us if it stays a skeleton."

"Foolish man! How silly you are to worry. We have our knowledge, and we know better than you," said the three scholars.

Up stepped the scholar of forms. "Now for the form!" he shouted. Then he waved his hands and chanted his secret mantras, and slowly he formed the muscles and the skin.

Subuddhi recognized the beast.

"Oh, my valued friends. Look at it now. This is a lion. It is a dangerous animal. If you value my judgment and common sense like other people in the village do, then please listen. Let us walk on."

But the scholars were so greedy for fame and so certain they were smarter than Subuddhi that they would not listen.

"What do you know? What have you studied or learned? What secrets have revealed themselves to you? You don't know much, but you know that we are smarter than you, so please stay quiet."

Then it was the turn of the scholar of life force itself.

"I will give the beast the puff of life. I will mutter my spells and chants, and then poof, puff, give it the breath of life," he said.

Subuddhi would not stand silent.

"My friends, this is a lion. A lion that eats people! If you give it a poof and a puff, then it may come to life and eat us all up. It is a *lion!*"

But the scholars were so excited by their success and so proud of how much they had done that their pride had blinded them to their friend's good advice.

"How dare you demand respect for your puny knowledge!" they said to him. "You are lucky we even let you come along. Everything you ever learned is nothing compared to our knowledge, and so of course we cannot respect your foolish demand."

"And so," said the scholar of the life force, "I give the breath of life. First, the chants."

He chanted.

"Then the poof," he said.

He gave the lion a poof of air.

"Now," he said, "for the puff of life."

But before he could puff, Subuddhi interrupted one last time.

"Oh great one, please pause a moment so that I might climb this nearby tree."

The scholars laughed at Subuddhi. "Yes, we will wait," they said, "so the fraidy-cat can run away. If you were smart like us, you wouldn't be so afraid."

So Subuddhi climbed the nearby tree. And when he was at the tip top, in branches so thin no lion could climb them, he shouted down that he was ready.

"And so," said the third scholar, "I give the puff of life! *PUFF!*"

The next day, Subuddhi came back to their village alone. When the villagers asked him why he came back so soon, he explained that he no longer wanted to travel. When they asked him what happened to the scholars, he told them the story of how the scholars had brought a lion back to life, how the newly alive lion was naturally very hungry, and how it ate them all.

"I tried to tell them to first climb a tree," said Subuddhi, "but they refused to learn from me."

LESSONS OF THE HEART

This very old story is often told to make the point that common sense is just as important as book learning. This is true. But it is also true that if the three scholars had simply shown respect to their friend and listened to him, then the lion would not have eaten them. It is a fine thing to be smart, and it is fine to be proud of it. But as these three scholars learned, there are many kinds of smart. One of the smartest things to do is to listen to others and to respect their knowledge and opinions. Too much pride was the scholars' mistake.

Story Notes

This is one of the ancient Panchatantra (also Pañcatantra or Pañca-tantra) stories of India. These comprise five books of animal fables and stories of magic. In all, there are about eighty-seven stories that were written around the fourth century AD. They have been trans-lated into many languages, including English. For example, a version of this story appears as "The Lion Makers" in Arthur W. Ryder's 1925 translation *The Panchatantra of Vishnu Sharma.*

SOCRATES AND THE ORACLE

a story of the humility of the founder of the Golden Age of Greek philosophy

A long time ago before there was science and before many people even knew how to read, there was a great city called Athens in the country we now know as Greece. The people of Athens were Greeks. Today, Athens is still a great city. Greeks have occupied it for thousands of years. Of all the people who ever lived in Athens, the most famous is a poor, ugly teacher named Socrates [SAH-kruh-TEEZ]. He lived in Athens more than 2,000 years ago. Socrates is remembered for many things, but perhaps strangest of all is that he is known for knowing what he did not know. The story of this riddle starts in a place called Delphi.

When the Greeks from long ago wished to know the answer to a question, they traveled to a holy place known as Delphi. There they found a priestess of the god Apollo.

She was known as the Oracle at Delphi. The Oracle would answer people's questions, but her answers were always in riddles. For example, once a great king came and asked her if he should invade another kingdom. The oracle told him, "If you do invade, then a great kingdom will be destroyed." The king attacked, thinking that he would destroy the kingdom of his enemy. The king lost, and instead *his* "great kingdom" was destroyed when he attacked a foe he could not beat. So the Oracle's answer was right, but only if the listener knew how to interpret it.

Socrates was a man who loved learning above anything. Sometimes he would stand without moving for hours while he thought about a hard problem. He talked with all the people of Athens, from the richest to the poorest. From anyone and everyone, he learned whatever they might know that he did not. If there was something no one knew, then he tried to find the answer. For Socrates, everything in the world was a question. His life was a search for the answers. But this sort of thing does not pay a lot of money. So Socrates was also poor. It was lucky for him that one day someone traveled to Delphi and asked the Oracle, "Who is the wisest man in Greece?" The Oracle answered simply, "Socrates." When this news reached Athens, the people were surprised. But they were pleased that the Oracle gave a straight answer for a change. Finally, they thought, the Oracle was speaking clearly. There was no doubt that this "Socrates" was the wisest man in Athens. This did a lot for Socrates' reputation and his fortune. Before the Oracle gave this answer, hardly anyone knew who Socrates was.

After the Oracle answered, everyone wanted to learn more about him. Many people wanted to pay him to become their teacher.

The problem was that Socrates did not understand the Oracle's answer. When someone told him about what the Oracle had said, he knew it had to be a mistake. He had spoken with many knowledgeable people in Athens. Almost any doctor knew more about healing. The farmers knew more about farming. The smiths knew more about metals. The merchants knew more about money and so on. How could he be the wisest man? As he always did whenever he was faced with a mystery, Socrates puzzled and puzzled on this problem. He finally realized what the Oracle must have meant. Whenever Socrates spoke with a knowledgeable person, he became aware of just how little he knew. But no one else in Athens bothered to try to learn from people outside their own areas of knowledge. All the experts thought their expertise was enough to make them the wisest. The healers thought they were the wisest because they knew about healing. The smiths thought they were the wisest because they understood metals. So it was with each group. Only Socrates valued all the knowledge that others had. Only Socrates understood that his knowledge was just a small drop in the pool of what could be known. "Thus," said Socrates, "if the Oracle says I am wise, it is for this one reason only: I know that I am not wise." From this the people of Athens and all of the smug "experts" learned that only the wisest people appreciate their limitations and allow for the fact that they can be wrong.

In the end, the simple answer of the Oracle was another riddle. It was such a hard riddle that it took the wisest man in Athens even to recognize that it was a riddle. And he solved it because he knew what he did not know.

LESSONS OF THE HEART

The insight that allowed Socrates to unravel the mystery of the oracle was his own humility in the face of all the things he had yet to learn. Confucius expressed the wisdom of this attitude when he remarked, "When you know a thing to recognize that you know it; when you do not know a thing to recognize that you do not know it; that is knowledge." Only once we recognize our limitations can we learn by listening to the viewpoint of another. If we believe we have nothing to learn, then nothing is what we will learn.

Story Notes

This, of course, is a story more than 2,000 years old and is purportedly based on true events. What we know about Socrates comes primarily from the comic poet Aristophanes; the soldier-historian Xenophon of Athens; and Socrates' extraordinary student, the philosopher Plato.

PROUD KING ROBERT OF SICILY

a king learns that value comes from your nature, not your station

In a far country, fair Sicily by name, in a year ages past, a king dwelt in rest and ease and fame.

King Robert had great wealth and many troops and servants too numerous to count. His family was a proud one. His older brother was Pope Urban in Rome, and his younger brother was Emperor Valmond of mighty Germany. Ships brought Robert goods beyond measure, and his taxes took a share from every ship. He hoarded his money in a huge treasury and spent his money only on his own glory. He bought for his table special delicacies from far across the sea, just to hear the flattery of those he invited to dine. He wore fine silks and embroideries, and he thrived on the fawning compliments his appearance drew from those around him. His subjects struggled to get by and were very poor. But King Robert felt it should be enough for them that they could be proud of having such a magnificent king living in such high style in a fancy palace.

Proud King Robert also thought he was right about everything, and he expected everyone to agree with him. If he gave a command, no one dared be slow in obeying it. In fact, he considered himself to be so important that no one was allowed to speak to him unless he gave permission first. To waste his time by speaking out of turn would bring swift punishment. And if he ever made a mistake or did some wrong, no one was brave enough to say so. The very thought of what King Robert might say about them had kept many a noble lord awake, tossing and turning in the night. So Robert lived in royal pride, thinking nothing of his responsibilities to those on Earth or those in Heaven. He went to the chapel at prayer time just because he wanted to see the expensive stained-glass windows, beautiful carvings, and jewel-encrusted chalices that he himself had paid for. He had even come to believe that the church was for his glory and not for God's.

One evening he was dozing in the palace chapel. He was thinking lazily of how rich he had to be to pay for such a fine and golden chapel. As he sat there, half asleep, he heard the priests chant a line in Latin. He had heard the line many times before. He did not understand Latin and never understood the line, or cared to understand it. For some reason on this night he asked a young priest about the line.

"You there," he said pointing to a priest, "what does that mean? The line they just sang."

The priest trembled because the king had asked him a question. His voice shook as he replied.

"Do you mean *'Deposuit potentes de sede, et exaltavit humiles,'* sire?" said the priest.

"Yes, yes, whatever. The 'humily, huma huma' line, whatever it was," said the king, sounding annoyed.

The priest was very scared. The king seemed to be mad at him. It took all his courage to reply, in as steady a voice as he could, "That line means, 'God has put down the mighty from their seat, and has risen up the low down.'"

Proud King Robert was not pleased. The thought that anyone would try to do this to him was not a happy one. It was not even a thought his pride would let him accept.

"It's good for you that this line is sung only in Latin and by priests whom nobody listens to or cares about. Anyone else who sang them would be jailed as a traitor to the king. Not only that, but the lines are pure folly and foolishness. There is no power that can push me from my throne!"

The frightened priest bowed low and backed away as quickly as he could. The gentle, peaceful, quiet singing continued, and King Robert calmed down. As he slumped in his chair, he fell asleep. He dreamed of how powerful he was and the delight he would have crushing anyone who tried to take away his throne.

For what seemed like a long time, King Robert dozed in the chapel. He did not know how long he slept. His sleep was heavy, and when he woke the services were over, the chapel was empty, and the room was nearly dark. The only light was a candle here or there burning in front of a statue of a saint.

King Robert was angry that his servants would allow him to be left alone. He muttered to himself that someone was going to pay for this as he strode to the door. When he pulled on the chapel door, it was locked. And he did not have the key. He pounded on the door, he cursed the door-keepers, and he shouted. At last the caretaker who kept all the keys arrived. He called out, "Who is it?"

"You fool!" shouted King Robert. "It is your king! Open this door right now if you want to keep your head!"

The caretaker was scared, but not for his head. He did not recognize the voice, and he assumed that some drunk or madman had got loose in the chapel. So he carefully opened the door and peeked in. The king, whom the care-taker thought to be a madman, rushed past. The caretaker did not realize his error because he saw a dirty, grimy, smelly man all dressed in rags, shouting and running away.

"Stop that man!" shouted the caretaker to the palace guards.

But before the guards could stop Robert, whom they also thought to be a madman, he was past them, running straight to the great banquet hall so he could scold the servants who'd left him behind.

Robert burst into the hall raging and raving. As he came in, he saw that a magnificent feast was taking place. All the finest foods and the happiest and most entertaining company were there. The people were dressed their best, laughing and eating with great merriment. And there at

the head table, at his table, and sitting in his throne was . . .
him! Wearing his crown, wearing his robes, and wearing a
face that looked exactly like him was another King Robert,
an imposter King Robert. Had King Robert looked at this
other more closely, he perhaps would have seen the heavenly light that shone upon him, and how he moved with
almost angelic grace. But Robert did not see this, because
in his pride and anger he was blind to everything except the
sight of someone sitting in his throne.

"Who are you?" one the noblewomen asked ragged
Robert.

"I am King Robert of Sicily, you fool. Use your eyes.
And who is the one you sit next to? What imposter dares to
wear my crown, sit in my throne, and eat my food? Speak
up, you fraud!"

At this, several of the noblemen and knights rose and
began to draw their swords.

"Stay your hands," said this second king. He looked at
ragged Robert and said, "No, you are not king. But you may
be the king's jester. Your role will be to amuse the court at
our pleasure. You shall wear the jester's cap and bells, carry
the jester's foolish scepter, and your royal courtier shall be
the jester's own ape."

Royal officers then took ragged Robert away and carried
out the orders. When Robert woke the next morning, just
for an instant he thought, "It was only a dream." Then he
rolled over and saw next to him the rude figure of the ape.
Robert was lying in straw, in a stable, with his bell cap and
a fool's scepter hanging by his head. It had been no dream.

Days passed, and then weeks. Under the rule of the angelic new king of Sicily—whom everyone believed to be the true king—the people were happier than ever. He was kind to them now, ruling them with wisdom and generosity. The people suffered no more wants and were prouder of their king than ever before.

Meanwhile, ragged Robert had been forced to give in to his new role. He had to wear the jester's hat, carry the fool's scepter, and act the part of a fool if he was to eat. And always he had with him the ape, whom he came to hate. But they could not force him to be happy or entertaining. He was the most sullen and silent and sad fool the court had ever seen. And sometimes the new king would come to him, in some quiet moment, when no one was around and ask, "And who are you today?" Every time, ragged Robert would raise his head, his fool's bells jingling in the silence, and with haughty pride in his voice he would say, "I am the king!"

So it went, for weeks and months, until three years had passed. Pope Urban sent word to his brothers the king of Sicily and the emperor of Germany to come to Rome for a great conference during the week of Easter. Both rulers agreed to come. So the current king of Sicily called together his soldiers, noblemen, and servants. He gave rich presents to one and all and announced that they would travel to Rome together. A bright pageant was formed and traveled across lovely Italy, making it even lovelier with their passing. There were bright plumes and fur-lined cloaks, ermine and gold, tiaras and crowns, jewels and jewelry, music and laughter all along the way. And the people of the countryside all cheered the good king on his way, sighing in wonder at his beautiful guests. Then at the end of the procession, the country folk laughed to see the sad jester, with his floppy belled crown and his fool's scepter, riding on a donkey. Around the donkey was the sign "King Fool," and next to fool Robert was the ape, his "duke." The fool Robert sat there so sad and serious looking that the people thought he was playing out a heartsick role as a joke, and so they laughed all the more. And as he passed he heard the people shout out in mockery, "All hail the king! Long live the King of Fools!"

When they arrived at the Pope's city, the Pope greeted them in St. Peter's Square with ceremony and pomp. The trumpets blared, and the sky was filled with rose petals. Then the Pope gave his blessings to his brothers, to their company, and to all those dwelling in their lands. Then, as he moved to embrace his brothers, a commotion rose in the crowd. Bursting through the crowds, and through the Pope's Swiss Guard, came a wild-eyed figure. It was the jester. He was calling to the Pope and to Emperor Valmond of Germany.

"Your holiness, Pope Urban, or Ortho as I knew you when we were boys! Royal Valmond—Val, my good brother. It is I. It is Robert. Do you recognize me? Embrace me, brothers."

But both emperor and pope looked at the jester with a stranger's eyes. They were even somewhat frightened by his wild look, and so they pulled back from him.

"Brothers, what is wrong?" cried the jester. "Look at me in my eyes. Do you not see we are kin? You cannot abandon me too. Not my own brothers."

As he spoke, his brothers looked at him with pity and sadly shook their heads. Then the Pope's Swiss Guards seized him and gently led him away. He heard Emperor Valmond, his own brother, turn to the current king of Sicily and say, "I will not judge, for I suppose in Sicily you have your own ways. But it seems to me, brother, a strange sport to keep a madman as your fool at court."

That night, fool Robert lay in his rough bed and moaned in sorrow. "How can I have come to this?" he cried aloud. "Why, oh why, could such a thing happen to me? My own brothers have turned from me. I was sure that they would recognize me. In my heart, I knew that they would. But they did not! My hope is gone. My life is gone. All that I was is gone forever. I shall ever be a fool. How could have I fallen so low after but a few hours' nap?" As he sobbed, he tore at his hair, wrung his hands, and beat his fists bloody on the wall. For long minutes he sobbed silently, with only the words "so low . . . so low . . ." whispering from his lips.

Then, at this lowest point, he heard the Easter week prayers coming from outside. He thought of the priest's lines, almost forgotten all these years: "God has put down the mighty from their seat . . . ." He thought to himself, "And so he has put down this fool." Then, for some reason, his heart rose up from its lowest point as he listened to the singing and thought of Him who had been put low, who had allowed himself to be humbled, and who, in doing so, was himself raised up by his sacrifice for others. Fool Robert ceased his sobbing and was able to lie down. Just before he drifted to sleep, it seemed, just maybe, that a wry smile touched his lips.

And so the visit ended, and on Easter Monday the royal train set out on their return trip for Sicily. Renewed by their spiritual rites with the Pope, the attendants and noblemen were even more wonderful and lovely than before. Again the people turned out to wave and cheer and "ooh" and "ah" as they passed. They remembered the jester and waited for him. This time when they called out, "Long live the king," he seemed to, just a little, raise up his scepter and shake his bells in response. And once or twice someone saw him pat Duke Ape with what might have been affection.

When at last they had reached Sicily once more and all were settled in their rooms, the word came to the jester. The king, the angelic and kindly king, wished to see him.

Fool Robert grabbed his hat and his scepter and answered the call. He entered the room where the good king sat on the throne. No one else was there. The king beckoned to the jester to approach closely.

As Robert drew near, the king asked, "And who are you today?"

Fool Robert shrugged and said, "You know better than I."

"Yes, that is so," said the king, "but I want to know what you say. I want to hear it from you."

Robert gave the answer as he was bidden.

"Whatever I am, I am no longer a proud king. Let me therefore be the jester that you say I am. And so at last I know that I am truly a fool, and so have I ever been. Now that I shall be a fool, I shall be as fine a fool as fools can be, for the good spirit of the people and the glory of my God. And in being such a fool, then foolish I shall no longer be. For foolish are those of us who walk beneath the heavens— the strong, the wise, the powerful, and the rich who do not contemplate our temporary state. Foolish are those who think themselves like God when they are, in so thinking, but fools. Truly it is said that the mighty will fall, the strong will falter, and so our pride must be in our devotion to righteousness, not in our success. And so I say now, I am no king, but I am as you say that I am—a fool—and you are my liege."

"Ah, but you misname me," said the other. "I am not king." The other paused and seemed to grow taller as he continued, "I am an angel, and you are . . ."

A holy light spread through the room until Robert was blinded. A holy music lifted up his spirits, and he seemed to be lifted up in body as well. Then Robert found himself in his robes, on his throne, and coming from the air he heard, "You are the king!"

Then Robert understood that what could be laid low could be lifted up again. He also understood a lot more, especially the foolishness of his own pride. And when his noblemen and servants came into the throne room, it was a better Robert, a humbler Robert, a good Robert whom they found kneeling in thankful prayer. From that day on Robert was as good a king as the angel had been. So his subjects had no further reason to complain. And they didn't even mind the strange quirk their king had developed: whenever he sat on his throne, he kept next to him an ugly, hairy, extremely well-fed ape named "Duke."

LESSONS OF THE HEART

Excessive pride hurts not only those around us but also ourselves. King Robert's pride caused him to mistreat everyone so that people feared him, but nobody really liked him or admired him. His pride also made his own people suffer, which is exactly the opposite of what he was supposed to do as king. Additionally, his pride blinded him to what was best for him and kept him from seeing that things like love and compassion and faith are much more important than earthly wealth and power. The loss of that wealth and power, which allowed him to lose his pride, was the best thing that ever happened to King Robert of Sicily.

Story Notes

This story was first told in the late fourteenth century as "Robert of Cisyle." It was made into epic poems in the nineteenth century. In William Morris's 1868 poem *Earthly Paradise*, it is called "The Proud King." In Longfellow's 1863 *Tales of a Wayside Inn*, it appears as "The Sicilian's Tale; King Robert of Sicily." The opening lines in our version are a near quote from the first three lines of Morris's poem.

COURAGE

First, we need to understand that courage is not the lack of fear but rather the willingness to act in spite of fear. Next, we must understand that all of the other virtues depend on courage.

In order to recognize true courage, we must not fail to realize that courage comes in various forms.

There is of course the courage of soldiers in battle and the courage of police officers and firefighters facing dangerous situations. Then there is the courage of those who stand up to a bully.

But not all acts of courage involve fear of bodily harm. There is courage in the face of fear of failure, fear of ridicule, fear of the unknown, and fear of new things. There is also the quiet courage of someone facing a terminal illness or someone facing life after the death of a loved one.

Courage is what allows us to act on the other virtues. In fact, without courage we can become so paralyzed that our virtues do no good whatsoever. For instance, to be compassionate yet not have the courage to seek justice is to fall short of true compassion. On the other hand, courage for its own sake is simply bravado. It is pointless posturing. Thus, to be meaningful, the other virtues must be accompanied by courage, and courage must be accompanied by one of the other virtues.

Minnie shows the courage to take responsibility for others.

THE COURAGEOUS SCHOOLTEACHER OF NEBRASKA

a true story about a teacher who saved her students' lives with clear thinking and courage in the face of danger

Life is full of boring, ordinary days. But sometimes, as Minnie Freeman was to find out, a day changes from ordinary to terrifying in the snap of a finger. And just like that, your life is changed forever.

January 12, 1888, in Ord, Nebraska, started off like any another Thursday. The only thing different was that the weather was warmer than usual, given that it was the middle of winter in the middle of Nebraska. For most of the week the weather had been very cold—so cold that the children would not go outside to play even though they were used to cold winters. In fact, it had been so cold that most of the children stayed home rather than try the long walk to school. But on January 12 the sun shone warm enough that the kids were able to go outside, to play a little, and to attend school.

Back in those days, in that part of Nebraska, the schools were not much like the ones we have now. The schoolhouse had just one room, and all the children learned from the same teacher. Minnie Freeman was one of those teachers, responsible for thirteen children, even though she was only nineteen years old herself. On this day she arrived in the morning to get ready and to start the fire in the iron schoolhouse stove. Although the temperature was now above freezing, it was still winter and the schoolhouse had to be heated if the students were going to be able to study. The old one-room schoolhouse in Ord had no gas heat, and in those days nobody had electricity. So all Minnie had to keep her school warm was a stove that burned logs of wood. In fact, Minnie's schoolhouse was so simple and poor that the roof was made of sod. This meant that while the walls were wood, the roof was covered with thick mats of dirt and roots instead of the shingles we use now. So it was important to get the fire lit, even on a day like January 12, 1888, a day that started sunny but did not end that way.

As the children straggled into school, some late because they had been playing with their coats off for a change, Minnie had them take their seats. The oldest child was just a few years younger than Minnie, and the youngest was only five. It was warm enough inside the schoolhouse, with its little stove, that the children could study without wearing coats. So they hung up their coats and sat down to work. The coats they hung on the hooks were warm, but most of the children had not worn any extra layers of clothes, or even scarves, because the sun was shining so brightly.

Everything was fine, everything was ordinary, and everything was even boring—until about three in the afternoon. Right about that time, Minnie looked outside and saw something unexpected. Dark clouds hung on the northwestern horizon. Something about them, the way they moved and the way that they sort of shimmered, caught her attention. She didn't know then that on the other side of that line of clouds people were fighting for their lives. She didn't know that in a couple hours she would be too. Right now all she saw was some odd-looking weather.

Curious, Minnie told the children to keep studying while she stepped outside. The air was perfectly calm for a few short minutes. Then out of nowhere dark clouds formed right overhead and then stretched across the sky. Before Minnie could even think about dismissing school and getting the children home, the air was filled with a fine snow, as powdery as sifted flour. Then there was a sudden shift in the wind, and it blew with a terrible violence. Minnie hurried back inside and closed the door against the cold.

The temperature dropped suddenly, even inside. When Minnie looked through the little windows and saw the blizzard, she knew that she could not send the children home. She knew that in weather like this, when the snow is so fine and the wind is so fierce, it is called a "whiteout." In a whiteout, people cannot see even a foot in front of them, and they can hear only the howling of the wind. Minnie had heard of experienced adults who had gotten lost in a blizzard like that and perished in the cold. She was not going to let that happen to her students.

So Minnie told the children to get their coats on and come next to the little stove so they could huddle together to keep warm. Her plan was to stay in the shelter all night long if necessary. She didn't have a lot of wood, but she thought she might be able to break up the chairs and desks to burn if need be. As they huddled there, the wind grew even stronger. They could feel the gusts coming through the flimsy roof and the cracks in the old walls. The schoolhouse rattled and creaked and shook so much they thought it would blow down around them. For an hour this went on, everyone huddled together trying to stay warm, the little ones crying in fear. After another hour they were crying because they were now hungry as well as scared. Minnie was just wondering how they would get anything to eat when it happened: the door blew in.

The schoolhouse door was not very strong, so the weak latch had given way, and the door had flown off its hinges. In rushed the punishing wind. Minnie and a couple of the older children were able to get the door back in front of the hole and prop it with a desk or two, but it didn't do much good. Meanwhile, the wind coming from the door had gotten under the roof and blown off part of one corner.

Minnie now faced a choice that no one should ever have to face.

They could do two things: they could stay, or they could go. Less than a half-mile away was a sturdy farmhouse that was warm and safe. But in a whiteout like this, a total and complete whiteout, even a few yards was far enough to get you lost and killed. So a half-mile was a long, long way away. But if they stayed, they might not be safe with the door gone and the roof going.

The children were screaming in cold and fear. The fire was flickering in the wind, almost going out. The wind was howling like a pack of mad dogs. And the walls and ceiling groaned and popped and creaked so much that poor Minnie could not even hear herself think. It would have been easy to let fear take over. It would have been easy to huddle there and cry in panic. Many people would have. But not Minnie. In all the chaos, she calmed down and thought the problem through carefully.

Minnie reasoned that if they stayed with the door gone, the wind would continue to eat at the roof, and before long the roof would go. With the roof gone, they were doomed. But the longer they waited, the colder it got and the weaker they felt. If they were to go, it was now or never. Minnie figured it out: their only chance to live was to take a chance of dying in the blizzard. They had to go, and right away.

Minnie was scared—not just for herself but for the children she cared for so much. They depended on her, and she had never done anything like this before. But the children needed Minnie to be brave, so Minnie decided she must be brave.

Minnie went to a desk and got a ball of twine. She said to the children, as loud as she could in that wind, "Children, not a half-mile that way is safety and warmth. We cannot stay here, so we must go there. I will tie this rope around each one of us so no one gets lost. If anyone of us stops, for whatever reason, to rub their hands or to get up from falling, then we will all stop. All of us together will go on together, we will stop together, and we will make it together."

Minnie paired the children up so that the oldest was with the youngest, the second oldest with the second youngest, and so on. Each person in a pair was tied to his partner. Minnie herself planned to carry the five-year-old. She tied the pairs to one another and then to her. Before they stepped out into the pitiless blizzard, Minnie turned to the children and smiled, saying, "It will be okay. We will be cold for a while, but we will make it. Remember, anyone stops and we all stop. And think about how warm we will be in a little while and how, years from now when you are grown up, your grandchildren will all come to you and beg you to tell the story of what we are about to do." She paused and then said, "Now, let's go!"

With that they pulled the desks away and headed into the blinding wind.

It was the steady wind that helped save them. In that storm, they could only see a few feet in front of them, and they would have gotten lost if Minnie had not used her head. Minnie knew that the wind was blowing from the direction of the house they were going to. So she kept the wind in her face, and that way she did not get lost. Children fell, and some of them turned the wrong way, but Minnie was always there. She stopped the group and turned the child or helped him up, keeping all the others together, and they were off again. Drifting snow and blowing winds buffeted them. But Minnie never wavered or despaired. She stayed focused on staying together and moving ahead.

They reached the farmhouse after what seemed like an endless night. They made it in safely and ate a warm meal. Some very worried parents joyfully hugged their children the next day.

After the story of their ordeal got out, Minnie was celebrated as a heroine. The education association of Nebraska awarded her a gold medal. She had a song written for her. Someone made a statue of her head and sent it around the entire country so people could see it. More than eighty men asked her to marry them, and she turned them all down.

Minnie herself thought all the fuss was unnecessary. She wrote about herself that she had not done "anything heroic or unusual" and that everything she did was "in the simple line of duty to those placed in her care." Quoting from a poem, she praised the "Great Spirit" who had guided them "through the desert and illimitable air, Lone wandering, but not lost."

LESSONS OF THE HEART

It takes great courage to face death. It takes even more to take responsibility for the lives of others. Courage is an essential virtue because often it is courage that makes the other virtues possible. Courage is not a lack of fear but rather the ability to take action even when we are afraid. And action is required if the other virtues are to have any effect. Had Minnie not had courage, all her compassion for the children would have done them no good. Fortunately, she not only had the courage to face pain and danger and fear but also the courage to make a difficult decision. She was levelheaded in the face of a deadly threat and made a tough choice that had to be made. In doing so, she saved the lives of those who were counting on her. For the truth is that, had they stayed in the schoolhouse, they likely would have died since the roof did blow off not long after they left. Sadly, many other people perished that day, on January 12, 1888, the day of a storm that is now known as "The School-house Blizzard."

Story Notes

This is based on a true story. A compilation of letters about the 1888 "Schoolhouse Blizzard" can be found in the book *In All Its Fury* (W. H. O'Gara, J & L Lee Co., 1947). Be warned that many stories from that day do not have happy endings. You can see a Venetian glass mural of *The Schoolhouse Blizzard of 1888*, showing Minnie and the children, on the west wall of the north bay in the Nebraska State Capitol Building in Lincoln, Nebraska.

THE GIRL WHO SAVED HER BROTHER

*a true Cheyenne story of courage
and love in the heat of battle*

American soldiers and Cheyenne Indians fought a battle near Rosebud Creek in Montana during the summer of 1876. Americans called this The Battle of the Rosebud because of where it was fought. The Cheyenne people named the battle in honor of what someone did: "The Fight Where the Girl Saved Her Brother."

The battle started when General Crook of the American army entered the last land left to the Native tribes in order to capture them. At Rosebud Creek, he met the united forces of Sioux and Cheyenne warriors. The Natives were in high spirits since the great Sioux holy man, Sitting Bull, had foreseen their victory in a vision. The warriors, who were all men, prepared themselves with holy dances and songs. Some men belonging to famous warrior societies vowed to fight to the death. All was made ready for war and killing. Crazy Horse of the Oglala [Oh-GLAH-la] Sioux shouted his famous war cry: "A good day to die and a good day to fight! Cowards to the rear; brave hearts—follow me."

The fight began. Many brave deeds were done and many brave hearts were proven. The battle swayed to and fro. But this was the Cheyennes' day. Their deeds outshone those of all the others, American soldier or Native. Among them was a brave young woman, Buffalo Calf Road Woman, who rode proudly beside her husband, Black Coyote. Her brother, Chief Comes in Sight, was also in the battle. She looked for him and at last saw him in great danger. He was surrounded. His horse was dead. The soldiers all around were aiming their rifles at him. He fought them off with courage and skill, but his sister knew that if nothing was done he would be killed.

Buffalo Calf Road Woman uttered a shrill, high-pitched war cry. Into the battle she raced her pony. Into the midst of her enemy she rode at full speed. Into danger she rode to save her brother. As she sped along, she uttered the spine-chilling, trilling, trembling cry to encourage her men during the fight. She rode to her brother and he leaped up onto her horse. Soldiers were firing their guns at them, but she was moving too fast to be hit. All the while, Buffalo Calf Road Woman laughed with the joy and excitement of battle. All the while, she sang her song. She turned her horse and rode out of the battle, up a hill and back to safety.

The Sioux and Cheyenne saw what she was doing—and so did the soldiers. All of them stopped fighting and watched the brave girl save her brother's life. The Native warriors raised their arms and set up a mighty shout that made everyone's hair stand on end. And even some of the soldiers threw their hats in the air and shouted "*Hurray!*" in honor of Buffalo Calf Road Woman.

When this happened, the battle had barely started. Hardly anyone had been hurt or killed. It is said that General Crook saw what Buffalo Calf Road Woman did and thought to himself, "If their little sisters fight like this, what will their warriors be like? Today is not the day to fight with these warriors. I will lose half my men if I do." General Crook then retreated, and the battle ended with fewer deaths than it might have otherwise.

LESSONS OF THE HEART

The Chinese Philosopher Lao Tzu observed, "Being deeply loved by someone gives you strength, while loving someone deeply gives you courage." This is a story of love and the courage it can bring. Once Buffalo Calf Road Woman saw her beloved brother in danger, there was no thought of her own danger as she rode to his rescue. Many who saw what she did thought that she had done the bravest deed of all—not taking a life but giving it.

Story Notes

This story is based on true events, and an account of them can be found at Wikipedia.org under the entries for "Battle of the Rosebud" and "Buffalo Calf Road Woman," where you can also see a picture of the heroine. Another account is found in *American Indian Myths and Legends* by Richard Erdoes and Alfonso Ortiz.

THE LONGEST RACE

a tale about the courage to overcome

They still tell the story of brave Pheidippides [fye-DIPP-i-duhs] the Runner; as they have told it for year upon year, centuries long past, some still tell that story. But I do not tell that story today. Of course, the story of how he ran is a famous one—he ran as one who is named "runner" must run, running for his city, which was under attack. In that story, Pheidippides the Runner was sent by his mother-city, Athens, to seek help in the coming fight against the Persian army. And so, some still say, he ran all the way to Sparta and then all the way back he ran: a distance of a hundred miles, and half again, all in a day. The news from Sparta was bad, and Athens had no one to help them in the coming fray. And, the story goes, Pheidippides fought, and he and his countrymen marched down to the beach at a place called Marathon, two dozen miles distant from

Athens, and there they won the battle, driving the Persians back into the sea.

Then the story, the story I do not tell today, goes on to report that Pheidippides the Runner was told, "Run, Pheidippides, run! One race more! Run back to Athens and tell them of our victory, how we have won the war!" With that, the story of Pheidippides, the story that others sometimes tell, ends with Pheidippides the Runner running one race too far, for he ran into Athens shouting, "Victory is ours! Joy!" and then died with joy on his lips. This is the story they tell, and how ever since, runners have run a race as long as that final race run by Pheidippides and named the race "marathon." And while I do not tell this story of Pheidippides, who earned the epithet "runner" if anyone has, I will tell you now of a marathon runner who, a hundred, a thousand, two thousand years later, ran, in a way, in the very footsteps of Pheidippides.

Ever since the ancient days of Athens, the nations of the world have held athletic games every four years. These are called the Olympics, and in these games athletes from all over the world come to compete for their country, to see who has the best athletes. The strongest throwers, the longest jumpers, and the fastest runners all come to compete in the Olympics. In 1968, John Stephen Akhwari [ahk-WAIR-ee], who was born on the shores of Lake Tanganyika in Africa, was sent by his country, halfway around the globe, to run the marathon against the rest of the world.

At the time, John Akhwari lived in a small village in Tanzania where he made his living, as did many of his friends, by farming the earth. John was a runner, one of the best in the world, but he did not make money from running. In those days, if you wanted to run in the Olympics and represent the pride of your country in competition, you were not allowed to get paid for running. So John did not run for prizes or make money from his fame; he ran only for the love of it and for the people of his country. For his part, his country provided the money to send John to the 1968 Olympics, which were held that year in Mexico City, Mexico—a continent and an ocean away from Lake Tanganyika in Tanzania.

So it was a grateful John Akhwari who stood at the starting line for the 1968 Mexico City Olympics, in the middle of the city at Zócalo [zoh-CAH-low] Square. More than 26 miles away was the finish line in the Olympic Stadium, where the runners would enter to the cheers of crowds waiting for the finishers. As John stood in Zócalo Square getting ready to start, he was more than 7,000 feet above sea level since Mexico City is nestled in among high mountains. At such a height, the air is very thin, and it is difficult to breathe if you are not used to it. This is why many of the other runners had prepared for the race by training at places that were also high up, so that their lungs would not hurt and their muscles would not cramp there in Mexico City. John had not been able to prepare in this way, but there he stood, more than a mile above sea level, determined to do his best.

As the race started John did well, for he was a first-class runner. It was not too long, however, before his muscles began to cramp. Still, John was a runner, a long-distance runner, and this means he was tough. So as much as the cramps hurt, and even though he fell back a little, John pushed himself to the middle of the pack. Then he had some very bad luck.

As John improved his position, he was among a large group of runners. He got tangled up with them. Someone accidentally tripped someone else, and John fell to the ground. Since he was running, he hit the ground hard. His leg was badly gashed, his knee was dislocated, and his shoulder was terribly bruised. The medics fixed him up the best they could with bandages and braces. He could barely stand on the knee, and he was in a lot of pain just from swinging his arm when he ran. And still there were the burning lungs and the cramps from the thin air. The medical people told John that he must drop out of the race. Many people did quit the race that day. Almost a quarter of those who started did not finish. John heard sensible voices—the medics, the voice of common sense—telling him the only sensible thing to do: "Quit." But John must have heard other voices that day: the voices of all those people back in his country who were counting on him. And maybe from far down the years he could hear the voices of those who extolled Pheidippides to run with news to Athens. Some- where, someone, some voice must have called, "Run, John, run!" And just like Pheidippides, John ran.

The winner of the 1968 Olympic gold medal for the marathon ran the whole 26 miles in just 2 hours and 20 minutes. About 3 minutes behind him came the silver medalist, and then right on his heels the winner of the bronze. The race was over—for an hour it had been over—when these three stood before the podium ready to hear the music and the cheers and to receive their hard won medals. Almost all the crowd had left the Olympic Stadium and come to the medal stand to watch the presentation. The TV cameras too had abandoned the stadium so they could broadcast the award ceremony. Almost no one was left at the stadium as the sun set, 3 hours and 20 minutes after the race had started. So only a small remnant of the crowd was in the stands as a lone and forgotten figure came limping in—his knee bandaged, his feet dragging, his shoulder in pain, his lungs on fire, but his head unbowed. In came, ever so slowly, John Stephen Akhwari. As he ran, and stumbled, and ran again around that stadium the crowd began to notice. And the cameras began to notice. And a cheer went up, building slowly, and the cameras recorded the most famous last-place finish in the history of the marathon.

No one tells the story of the men who won medals that day, and few can remember their names. But some still tell the story, some people like me still tell the story, of John Stephen Akhwari and how he finished his race, running when his body was no longer able to run, just like that Greek runner from so long ago. And while John Akhwari was not able to declare "Victory" or shout "Joy," he, like Pheidippides, is remembered for words he spoke after his run. When he was asked why he did what he did, when there was nothing to gain but hardship and pain, his answer was a simple one. With grit seldom matched since the days of Pheidippides, he said only, "My country did not send me 5,000 miles to start the race. They sent me 5,000 miles to finish the race."

LESSONS OF THE HEART

One of the most profound forms of courage is the courage it takes to do something not because it is brave, not because it will mean anything, but because it is the right thing to do. John Akhwari was never going to win that race. But he was bound to finish as best he could because this is what he had promised to do when his country sent him to Mexico City. He had the courage not only to face pain and to risk injury but also to keep going for no reason except that he felt that he owed it to himself and to his country.

Story Notes

This story is based on the widespread accounts of the efforts of John Akhwari in 1968. For those worried about him, he did recover and he did compete again at the international level. The official Olympics webpage describing the events of the 1968 marathon along with some footage of Akhwari's finish is www.olympic.org/news/marathon-man-akhwari-demonstrates-superhuman-spirit.

Although John Akhwari's story is one of our favorites, the authors' all-time favorite race-finishing story is found in Jim's book *Looking Around for God*. In the chapter "God at the Track Meet," Jim tells the story of his autistic son Ronald (Rick's brother), his performance at a track meet, and the reaction of the crowd. A YouTube video of Jim reading the story is found at youtu.be/8Kh8Dp8Eq1U (or search YouTube for "God at the Track Meet").

WORSHIPING WITH THE ENEMY

BY EWART A. AUTRY

*a true story about a young girl
having the courage to forgive*

It was a cold, bleak Sabbath morning when worshipers gathered at the Pine Grove Church, a small log structure nestled in a grove of majestic pine trees among the high hills of North Mississippi. Betty Elliott was among the worshipers. Blonde, beautiful, in her teens, Betty had been thinking sadly of her brothers as she'd walked the two miles to church. It was a time of war, and it had been rumored that two of her brothers were missing in action, which meant they were either dead or prisoners of war.

Betty, along with her neighbors, knew only bitterness for Yankee soldiers. When she rounded the last curve toward the church and saw that smoke was roiling from the building's humpback chimney, she smiled because she knew there would be warmth inside. She quickened her pace as the wind screamed through the pines.

Entering, she found a dozen old men, women, and children grouped before the fireplace. Hickory logs were crackling merrily, but there was no merriment on the faces of the worshipers.

By the time for the services to begin, the congregation numbered about thirty. Then the minister, a tall, gaunt man with thinning gray hair, arose and led the singing.

"Let us pray," he said as the singing ended. "Not only for ourselves and our loved ones, but for the enemy as well."

"Pray for the Yankees?" cried an old man whose boy had fallen in battle. "What do they care about prayer or God?"

"I don't know how much they care about prayer or about God," said the minister calmly, "but I do know that God cares about them. A man who can't pray for his enemies can't pray."

In the moment of silence that followed the prayer, there came the sound of galloping horses beating down on the wind. The minister looked out the north window. "It's Yankees," he said. "Maybe they'll pass on by."

But the Yankees didn't. Swiftly, they swept around the church and began to dismount.

"Let's all remain as we are," the minister said. "They'll soon let us know what they want."

In a few moments, the door was gently pushed open and a young Yankee captain stepped inside. "We're looking for a place to worship today," he said, removing his hat. "We would like to worship with you if you will permit us." He paused. "But we won't force ourselves on you. I shall wait outside for five minutes and give you a chance to discuss it among yourselves. If you decide 'no,' we'll be on our way." He bowed and stepped outside.

For a few moments there was complete silence inside save for the crackling of the fire.

"If we can't pray with our enemies, then what right will we have to pray at all?" asked an old man, echoing the minister's earlier comment. But most of the people kept quiet and seemed uncomfortable at the thought of worshiping with the Yankee soldiers who had invaded their homeland and killed their relatives. There was a little more discussion until the time was almost up. Finally, an old lady turned to Betty Elliott.

"Honey," she said, "you have likely suffered from the enemy as much as any of us. What do you say?"

Betty felt herself trembling as she thought of her brothers. Then she remembered what Jesus said: "Father, forgive them." She lifted her head. "Let them come in," she said.

The young men from the North came silently into the church. When they were seated, the minister asked if anyone among them could lead a song. A slender, dark-headed young man arose and began a song that was familiar to everyone. The strong voices of the soldiers united with those of the women, children, and old men. Then the captain led in prayer. He prayed not only for the folks back home but also for those in the war-torn land of the South. He prayed so earnestly that when he had finished, many eyes were wet with tears.

Then the service ended and the soldiers remained a while to talk of their folks back home. Finally, when they left, the captain turned and said, "Good-bye, and God bless every one of you."

As they galloped away, the minister said, "There goes a bunch of boys who hate war and love God as much as we do." Then he looked at Betty Elliott and said, "Young woman, we thank you for being brave enough to lead us to worship with our enemies."

As Betty walked home that day, she still felt the sadness and longing for her brothers, but she knew also that her hatred had died within the walls of that little church and that it would never come again.

LESSONS OF THE HEART

Sometimes it takes more courage to reject violence and hate than to embrace it. And it always requires more courage to forgive than to hold a grudge.

Story Notes

Betty Elliott was Ewart A. Autry's grandmother, James A. Autry's great-grandmother, and Rick Autry's great-great-grandmother.

COMPASSION

We are at our best as human beings when we act with compassion, but we understand that there's nothing easy about it. Compassionate people are often judged to be "soft" or "pushovers" or "unrealistic" or "impractical." That's why compassion also requires the virtue of courage to overcome the hardheaded realities of daily life that work against compassion.

The best definition of compassion is allowing the emotion of love to have free reign in our lives. This means simply caring about the welfare of other people, even people we don't know, and trying to help them when needed.

In competition, whether in sports, games, or business, the compassionate person always shows respect, support, and goodwill to his or her adversary, win or lose.

Compassion, which can be aroused easily, is often difficult to maintain; in fact, it is a great virtue precisely because it is not an easy one. If we want to maintain our compassion, we have to keep it in mind at all times. Without that vigilance, it's far too easy to convince ourselves that it's more sensible to have a hard heart.

The king learns that compassion is often better than revenge.

The Golden Deer

A Jataka Story

the Buddha is a magnificent Golden Deer
who teaches a king the lesson of
justice and compassion

Buddha, a soul that was always seeking for truth, was born into this world as a deer. His noble horns were as silver. His hoofs were bright and his coat was the gold of the sun. He lived along the banks of the Ganges [GAN-jeez] River, the most sacred river of India, in a grove of fruit trees.

A day's ride from this grove was the city of Benares [be-NAR-ees]. In this city there lived a young man named Moneyman, the son of a rich merchant. His father had given Moneyman everything except good sense. Moneyman spent all his time singing, dancing, drinking, gambling, and feasting. He did anything but work. He did nothing that might benefit anyone but himself.

While Moneyman was still young, his old father died. Moneyman did nothing to take over his father's work. Instead, he continued to spend money as quickly as ever. Of course, he was soon out of money and started to borrow so he could pursue his selfish pleasures.

When the moneylenders came to get their money back, they were angry to find out that Moneyman had nothing at all. All day, angry shopkeepers beat at his door and followed him through the streets. No one would lend him any more money, and he was unable to buy pleasures and entertainment.

"This is a terrible way to live," Moneyman thought. "I would rather be dead." So he shouted to the shopkeepers that he was going to retrieve a buried treasure he had buried by the Ganges. He then walked until he came to the banks of the Ganges and, while the astonished shop-keepers looked on, threw himself into the river. He was swept down the river out of sight.

Not far away, the Golden Deer was resting in the tall grasses when he heard a cry coming from the river. It was the sound of a drowning man, so he bounded off to help. He plunged into the rushing water and found Moneyman close to death and unable to swim. He bore the young man away from the river on his back. He cared tenderly for Moneyman among his grove of trees. He fed him the sweet fruit and nuzzled him with his body to keep him warm. After several days the man was, at last, feeling good enough to move about. After several more days, Moneyman was ready to leave the Golden Deer.

"Climb upon my back," said the deer, "and I will bear you to the road to the city. But you must swear that you will tell no one that you saw a golden deer. Do not let anything, not money or promises, tempt you to reveal that I am here."

The young man agreed readily and assured the Golden Deer that he would not betray such kindness. The deer took Moneyman and placed him on the road to the world.

So the young man headed back to the city in the land of Benares. As Moneyman ventured toward home, he realized that the Golden Deer had given him a fresh start. His creditors would not come looking for him. He could, if he was inclined, make a new life for himself.

On the very day that Moneyman left the Golden Deer, the queen of Benares had a dream. While she slept, she dreamed of a magnificent deer with a golden coat and silver antlers. In a voice as sweet as chimes, he spoke to her of truth, love, and beauty. When she awoke, the queen was haunted by her dream. She rushed to the chamber of her husband the king.

"I am certain that the deer was no simple dream. I know that he exists somewhere. I must see him in the waking world. His words were so wise, his voice so sweet. If I do not hear him speak again, I shall surely die."

The king loved his queen very much and could deny her nothing. He told her, "If the deer lives as far as Zanzibar, I shall find him for you."

The king gave orders right and left. In no time, an elephant was dressed in gold-embroidered cloth and led through the streets. On the elephant's back rested a golden box containing a thousand golden coins. Beside the elephant a servant walked with a tablet of gold on which was written the reward for the golden deer: the thousand coins, the golden box, the tablet, the elephant, and a village of the kingdom.

It so happened that the elephant was passing just as Moneyman returned to Benares. As soon as the young man heard of the huge reward, his mind was filled with thoughts of the pleasures he could have. Forgotten was the idea of a new life. Forgotten was his promise to the Golden Deer. Gratitude was drowned in Moneyman's heart as surely as he would have drowned in the river if not for the Golden Deer. "Take me to the king," he demanded. "I know where the Golden Deer can be found, and I claim the reward."

With Moneyman as their guide, the king and his soldiers set out to capture the Golden Deer. They quickly reached the peaceful grove where Moneyman had been nursed back to health. The pounding of their horses' hooves shook the ground. The Golden Deer knew they were coming, and when he looked out he saw hundreds of soldiers and, standing apart from them, the king.

"Only with the king will I be safe," thought the Golden Deer. He suddenly ran from the grove straight for the king.

The king was afraid when he saw the Golden Deer heading toward him. The king stomped his feet and shook his bow to scare away the deer. Still the Golden Deer came on. The king, in fear, knocked his arrow and raised his bow. "I must try to hurt him so he will stop," thought the king.

But as he was drawing the string, the deer called to him. "Fair king, do not shoot me."

The sound of that voice made the king drop his bow and stare at the deer in awe.

"Who told you where to find me?" asked the deer.

The king told the deer the story of the dream and the reward, and how Moneyman had brought them here as a guide. He then ordered his soldiers to bring Moneyman over to them.

The Golden Deer turned to Moneyman. "Is this how you repay me for saving your life? Is this how you keep your promise to tell no one about me? I should have pulled a log from the river rather than a man with so little honor!" said the deer. The deer then told the king about how he had rescued and nursed Moneyman almost on that very spot.

The king was angry. "A man so ungrateful that he would betray this miraculous deer who saved his life surely deserves to die." With that, the king picked up his bow and again prepared to shoot it. This time he aimed at Moneyman.

"Do not kill him," said the deer. "Even though he has betrayed me in the worst manner, I do not want him harmed because of me. No killing can be good; no good man can approve of killing. Revenge is easy. Mercy is greater. Let him go, and reward him as you have promised. That will be punishment enough. He will make his own."

The king, for the second time, stayed his hand because of the deer. "Pay off the villain and get him out of my sight," said the king. The delighted Moneyman was paid and sent back to the city, where he lived a life of pleasures with the reward. Never did he start his new life of good living. Never did he learn for himself the wise ways of the Golden Deer.

"It is easy enough to make promises," said the deer. "The difficulty lies in keeping your word."

"Ask me for whatever you wish, and, if you will come with me to Benares, I will grant it," said the king.

At this the deer asked for his safety and the safety of all the animals in the king's woods.

"So it shall be," said the king.

The king and the Golden Deer returned to Benares. There the king and queen listened for days to the deer. His speech was as wise as it was beautiful. The king did not forget his promise and announced safety for all the animals in his woods. The deer then returned to his grove along the river.

Before long, the people of the kingdom complained about the king's decree. "Since we cannot kill the deer, they come into our gardens and eat all of our food. We will starve quickly if nothing is done."

The king refused to change his decree. "Even if you drive me from the throne, I will not break my promise," he told them.

The people returned to their homes not knowing what to do. Away in the forest, the Golden Deer learned of what was happening. It so happens that the Golden Deer was himself treated as a king among the deer. He called them all together and spoke with them. "You must find your food in the woods and meadows. You must not eat the foods that men have planted for themselves." The deer did as the Golden Deer had asked them. So, long ago in Benares, man and beast lived together in harmony.

LESSONS OF THE HEART

Compassion is not reserved for only sympathetic people. Even liars and traitors are worthy of compassion. When the Golden Deer moderated the king's revenge with compassion, a truer justice was served. Moneyman got the money that had originally ruined him. His greed was his own punishment. Meanwhile, the compassionate justice and honesty that the deer and the king showed each other benefited them and the entire countryside.

Story Notes

This is an ancient story, being one of the Jataka tales. A Jataka story is a Buddhist story based on their belief in reincarnation. They believe that a soul is born again in other forms. The Jataka stories come from the life of Buddha before he was born as a prince of India. Specifically, this is Jataka 482, the Ruru Jataka of the Pali Canon. It has been published many times including in Rouse and Cowell's translation, *Jataka or Stories of the Buddha's Former Births*, printed by Cambridge University Press in 1901.

THE PAINTINGS OF HEAVEN AND HELL

a seeker of knowledge learns a lesson about kindness

Here's a small flourish; it's just for fun. Now for the story that's not yet begun.

Somewhere or other, I don't know where, there lived a sincere man named Zhi [JEE], whom his friends called Zhi the Ever Seeking because he always wanted to know the answers to any mystery. Since he was a boy, Zhi had sought to know the way of things and also more than just things; he wanted to know the spirit of the world that lies beyond things, the true nature of what is. He had learned of the trees and the birds and the secrets known to rocks and to clouds, and still he did not know enough. For two and thirty years Zhi, the Ever Seeking, had sought to know. After all these years, he decided that he at last knew almost all he wished to know of what we call the Earth. His thoughts then turned to the worlds other than this Earth. "What," thought Zhi, "is the world that is beyond our world? What of the land of eternal firmaments? What of Heaven and of Hell?"

So Zhi went forth to seek for the truth of Heaven and Hell. As he journeyed, he asked every living thing what it knew, for this was his favorite way of learning.

First he came to a farmer and asked, "Good sir, please tell, what is the difference between Heaven and Hell?"

"Ah," said the farmer, "that is easy to say. Heaven is the fall, with the crops all in, the cattle all fed, and hot tea steeping on the stovetop. Hell is the wild winds that sometimes come in spring, blowing down the new planted crop."

Zhi thanked the farmer and continued his travels.

Next, Zhi, the Ever Seeking, came upon a small bird. Zhi had learned much in his seeking and he knew the language of the animals. So he asked the bird about Heaven and Hell.

"Yes, I have flown to Heaven," said the bird. "It is a leafy tree in the gentle breeze, where the grubs come to you asking to be eaten. Hell is a long flight over a barren land that has no place to perch and that is prowled by hungry cats."

Again Zhi bowed low and thanked the bird, and he continued to seek for truth.

Next Zhi came upon an old dog and asked the creature about Heaven and Hell.

"Heaven is a warm spot in front of the fire, a bone to chew on, and a scratch between the ears. Hell is a long night outside, tied to stake in the rain."

Zhi thanked the dog, and on he continued, asking each person and each animal about Heaven and Hell. And each one he asked gave him a different answer. Zhi decided that whatever Heaven was, and whatever there might be in Hell, their true nature was more than all these particular things that had been told to him. "Each being I have questioned told me only what they imagine Heaven and Hell might be like. But none of them has seen the true nature of Heaven and Hell."

Zhi sought for the truth of these eternal places. He wanted to know what they were like deep down, what made them different in their very souls. He reasoned that to get to the true nature of Heaven and Hell, he must find those who, like him, were seekers. He decided he must consult the people who spent their lives in contemplation not of this world, not of rain and trees and bones, but of the firmaments and the true nature of the world.

So Zhi now sought a place where he might find those who study deep into the true nature of Heaven and Hell. As he traveled, he asked where he might find such people, and each person told him he should ask the monks in the old and lonely monastery high in the mountains. So Zhi, the Ever Seeking, walked a long way until he came at last to the Lonely Monastery.

As Zhi stood before the great oaken door of the Lonely Monastery, he looked in vain for a knocker. There was none. So he tried calling out. No answer came. As the night drew near, he laid his hand on the door and tried it. It was unlocked, for all are welcome in the Lonely Monastery. There is no answer to a call because the call need not be made. There is no knocker because the door is always open. The only bar to entry is the reluctance in the traveler's own heart.

As the doors swung in, Zhi came upon a wondrous and peaceful garden. The light of the setting sun touched the delicate leaves of the trees, which glowed like gentle torches, illuminating the courtyard. There were plants of many types, and Zhi was surprised to see some he did not recognize. Perhaps high in these mountains, he thought, they had plants from worlds beyond. Just then a young monk came to Zhi and greeted him politely.

"Welcome, worthy Zhi! Tidings and fair health to he who is known as Ever Seeking."

"I thank you for your gracious greeting and your gentle hospitality. Pray, how do you know my name?"

"We of the Lonely Monastery have heard of your coming for many months, and now we receive you with joyous arms."

The monk then led Zhi into a room, offering him simple food and hot tea and a soft bed. They seemed quite luxurious to Zhi after his many weeks on the hard and rocky pathways.

"Rest and make comfort tonight," said the young monk, "and tomorrow you may continue in your seeking. I will take you to see Ping, Master of Benevolent Repose.

You may then pose your question as you please. But know this: the answer may not come as quickly as you hope."

"Thank you," said Zhi, "and do not worry. I am patient. A seeker must always be patient."

The next morning after breakfast, the young monk came to Zhi. Without speaking a word, he took Zhi by the hand and led him into a small room with two chairs. The young monk gestured for Zhi to sit in one chair. On the opposite chair sat an old monk. He was dressed simply and seemed to doze with his pale head resting on his chest. His skin was as white and wrinkled as an unmade bed sheet. His hair was long and wispy and white, like a great mass of cloud sitting on his head. As he lifted his head, Zhi saw that the man's beard and mustache had the same color and lightness and seemed almost to float off his face. The face was a surprise, for while the monk was very old, his face was youthfully fresh and his eyes were bright.

"Greetings, and hail morning to you Zhi, the Ever Seeking."

"Honor to you, old father. Are you Ping, Master of Benevolent Repose?"

The old man gave a loud laugh, quite startling in such a small and quiet place. "Ha! I am called Ping, but I cannot say I am master of anything. If by Benevolent Repose you mean that I like to take long naps on warm afternoons, then that is me! But I am told, Ever Seeker, that you have for me a question."

Zhi got right to the question with no further delay, for he had come a long way to ask.

"Yes, Master Ping. I now seek the true nature of Heaven and Hell."

"You may know, venerable Zhi," said Master Ping, "that the true nature of those eternal places may not be known or understood in the usual way. The best way to seek their nature is to divine them through self-understanding. Yet I know you have traveled far and waited long. So I will take you to the next room, where I have a painting of the true nature of Heaven and Hell."

At this Zhi became excited. Until he saw the painting—for in the next room there was a painting divided into three panels. In front of it was a soft pillow to sit upon.

"Sit here on this pillow. Look at those three panels until you understand their meaning. Then tell me what is the true nature of the fourth panel," said Ping.

Zhi looked at the fourth panel. He had not noticed it before. It appeared blank.

"Is it not blank?" asked Zhi.

"That," said the Master, "is the question you must answer."

Zhi examined the three panels closely. In the first, he saw a group of people being led into a room. Tall stools awaited them, arranged around a circular pit. In the second painting the people were seated on the stools and seemed to have in their hands long chopsticks. The stools were about five feet apart and the chopsticks were at least that long. In the third painting a huge bowl of steaming rice had been placed in the middle of the circle of stools. The bowl was set inside the pit, which was as deep as the bowl.

Each of the diners was reaching down into the bowl with the long chopsticks. It took Zhi about a half hour of close examination to take in every detail of the paintings. Then he looked at the fourth.

"I still see nothing in the fourth," Zhi said.

"Looking will not tell you everything," said Master Ping. "You must understand what you see, and tell how it illuminates the natures of Heaven and Hell."

Master Ping then left Zhi sitting on the pillow, cross-legged. Zhi just sat there staring at the paintings and thinking. He sat there all through lunch, and through the afternoon, past dinner until, at bedtime, Master Ping entered the room. He asked Zhi what he had learned.

Zhi replied, "I see the diners in the first painting. They are anxious and very hungry. In the second painting, they anticipate the coming food and learn to use the clumsy chopsticks. In the third they sit with the big bowl far away, deep in the pit, and try to figure how to eat with the chopsticks so long and clumsy. I conclude: the fourth painting depicts the true nature of Hell. Each person is hungry and greedy for food, eternally they are hungry, but with only the long chopsticks they cannot feed themselves. As they try to bring the food into their mouths, it falls into the pit and they only get a little rice. They are doomed to be forever hungry and never able to eat. That is the true nature of Hell: to suffer the unsatisfied needs of this world, forever, in the next."

"What have you learned of Heaven?" asked Master Ping.

"Nothing," said Zhi.

"You have learned much," said Master Ping. "Come back tomorrow and you may learn the rest."

The next day Zhi ate a big breakfast, for he was very hungry, and once again he came to Master Ping, who took him to the room with the paintings. Again Zhi sat cross-legged. All day long he sat and thought of Heaven. He thought of all the help he had been given on his journeys and how finding kindness from strangers was the source of all his knowledge. Without this help, his seeking would have come to nothing. It was all day, but it seemed like no time at all, before Master Ping once again entered the room at bedtime.

"What have you learned today?" asked Master Ping.

"The paintings also depict Heaven."

"Why do you say so?" asked the master.

"Because in Heaven, in the blank panel the people are not so greedy that they think only of themselves. In Heaven people think of others and work together. The true nature of Heaven is benevolence, kindness, and deep concern for your fellow beings. This being so, I see now in the fourth panel the true nature of Heaven: in Heaven they feed each other."

"Your old seeking has ended," said Master Ping, "and now new seeking will begin."

LESSONS OF THE HEART

In many ways, we carry Heaven and Hell around with us in our own hearts. Which one we experience depends on our attitude towards the world and towards other people. Acting with greed and in selfishness is bound to be unsatisfying. Acting with kindness and compassion not only is its own reward but may also inspire others to act the same way. This sort of attitude helps us find a heavenly home here on Earth, in community with others.

Story Notes

This story has sources in Jewish, European Christian, Chinese, and Vietnamese traditions and is well known to American preachers.

THE MAGIC GARDEN

a story from the Steppes of Asia about compassion for the less fortunate

A long time ago in a faraway land there lived two friends named Asan and Hasan. Asan was a poor farmer who grew crops on a small farm. Hasan was a poor herdsman who kept a tiny herd of cattle. Between the two of them, they barely managed to keep going from one year to the next.

The wives of these two had died many years before, leaving each man with a single child. Asan had a loving daughter whom he cherished, and Hasan had a son who to him was the sun, the moon, and the stars.

One spring Hasan's cattle got sick. One by one they died off. Hasan worked every trick he knew to save the cattle, but the disease was too fast. Hasan's entire herd, which was not very large after all, was killed in just a few days.

After his last cow died, Hasan came to his friend in tears.

"Asan," he said, "here, take my hand. I thank you for your friendship over the years, but now I must say farewell. My herd is gone and without it I cannot make a living. It will not be long before I too will see the grassy steppes no more."

"Dear friend," cried Asan, "I will hear no such talk! Half of my heart is yours, so do not refuse half of my field. I give it to you. Take your hoe and scythe and come to work alongside me."

So Hasan became a farmer just like his friend. Although they had no more land, somehow through their teamwork the friends were able to feed two families off the land that used to feed only Asan's. Together they worked in rain and shine. And still they just eked by from day to day. Years passed like this until one day, as Hasan was digging in his half of the field, he struck something hard in the ground. As his hoe struck, he thought he heard a "clank." Excited and curious, Hasan dug out what he had struck—a pot of gold coins!

Hasan grabbed the pot, and with joyful tears he leapt and skipped and danced to the hut of Asan.

"Asan, I have great news!" he cried as he ran. "You are in luck! I have dug up a pot of gold. You are rich!"

Once Asan heard the story he smiled at his friend but admonished him gently: "I know how unselfish you are, Hasan, but this is too much. I do not own that gold. You found the gold in your half of the field."

"I know how generous your heart is, Asan," protested Hasan, "but when you gave me the land you did not give me what was buried beneath it. How could you give to me something you didn't even know about?"

"Dear friend," said Asan, "the riches that lie beneath the earth belong to those who toil above that earth. I will not take your gold."

On and on the two friends argued. Hasan refused to keep the gold for himself and Asan refused to take any from him. Finally, Asan had a wonderful idea.

"Hasan, it is clear that neither you nor I will keep this gold. But you have a son and I have a daughter. They have loved each other since they were children. They are old enough and would marry, so let us give them this gold. Let them be poor no longer."

Hasan agreed wholeheartedly with this plan. When they told the children, they were giddy with happiness. The wedding was held that very day. The boy and girl settled down on Hasan's land, and Hasan moved in with Asan.

The next day there was a knock at the door of the two fathers. When they opened the door, there stood their children with the pot of gold.

"We have been thinking," said the boy, "and it is not proper that children should keep what belongs to their parents. Our love is more precious to us than any money, so we need nothing more than we already have."

With that, he set the gold in the fathers' field and left. Once again Asan and Hasan started their gentle battle over who should take the gold. Finally, it was decided that the four of them should take the gold and their problem to a wise man who was well known for his honesty, fairness, and good sense.

They walked long and far across the grassy lands. They came at last to the hut of the wise man. It was a plain hut, sitting all alone on the wind-swept steppe. They humbly asked permission to enter and present their problem. After they entered, they greeted the wise man and his four pupils. The wise man asked them, "What problem would you have me solve?"

The visitors explained about their quarrel. When they finished, the wise man sat in silence. At length he turned to the oldest of his pupils and asked him what he would do.

"I would order that the gold be taken to the khan since all lost goods belong to him by decree," said the oldest.

"Hmm," said the wise man. "And what would you do?" he asked the next oldest.

"I would keep it myself, for the khan has no more need of gold," said the second.

The wise man said nothing but frowned. He posed the question to the third pupil who replied, "Since the gold is of the earth, to the earth I would return it. Bury the gold once more."

Here the wise man shook his head and turned to the youngest. "And what, youngster, is your suggestion?"

"Teacher, you will think me foolish. Forgive me. I have not been thinking very hard, but instead I answer from the heart. The first thought that came to me was that I would buy seeds, and with the seeds I would plant in the most barren part of the great plain a vast, shaded garden. Then all the tired and weary poor might rest there and enjoy its fruits."

"Aha," said the wise man, "you have answered well. Your decision is a just and fair one. Take this gold and go to the capital and buy the best seeds you can find. When you have returned, we will plant that garden. And may you and these generous people never be forgotten by those who enjoy the garden."

The young student put the treasure in a bag, slung the bag over his shoulder, and struck out for the capital and its marketplace. On he traveled, across the great plain for days without end. When at last he came to the city, he could not believe his eyes. The outer walls were higher than anything he had ever seen in his broad, grassy homeland. He made his way to the open space of the marketplace. He wandered for a time among the beautiful wares from far away and looked for a dealer of seeds. As he looked around, he heard the sound of caravan bells followed by screaming. He turned and saw an enormous caravan carrying a strange cargo. Instead of fine cloth or sweet spices, this caravan carried living things. The huge camels were laden down with thousands and thousands of live birds. Birds of the forest. Birds of the mountains. Birds of the steppes. Large birds, bright birds, small birds, dull birds. Every kind of bird that flew and sang was gathered here. And none of them was happy. They were tied by the feet, their wings dangling limp and crumpled, and above them floated clouds. The youth stared at these clouds, and for a time he could not tell what the clouds were made of until, all of a sudden, he realized that the miserable birds were losing so many feathers that feathers floated over the entire caravan like smoke from a fire. At each movement of the caravan, the birds beat their heads against the sides of the camels and cried out.

The young man's heart was full of pity. He was a man of the open lands, and he knew well how those birds must long for the open sky. But he would soon be returning to the grasslands, and they would never return to the sky. This thought was too much for his heavy heart. He approached the man who led the caravan.

"Who has doomed these magnificent birds to such torture?" he asked.

The leader replied, "These birds are for the khan. They are to be cooked and fed to the khan. He will pay us 500 gold pieces for them."

"That is ridiculous!" said the youth, "I know some of these birds and I know that their flavor is no good. Why should anyone pay so much for them?"

"The khan does not care if they taste good. He wishes only that the birds be hard to find and expensive. This way he can show off how much money he has. These birds will be highly prized since they come from far away. I expect no less than 500 gold pieces."

"I," said the youth in a sudden decision, "will pay you twice that. I will pay a thousand."

The caravan leader laughed and laughed until the youth opened the leather bag. Then the leader laughed no more.

At once he ordered his men to untie the birds. Immediately the marvelous birds rushed into the sky. So many of them there were that the sun was blocked. In the palace, the khan frowned because he could not read his book. He cried orders that torches should be brought. So many were the birds that the flutter of their wings sent a violent wind across the land. In the palace of the khan, the workers had just lit a torch when a wind came through the window and blew it out again.

For a long time the youth followed the birds with his eyes. He imagined that he too was in the air and free, soaring far past the walls of the city and across the plain to his home. With this thought he shuddered.

"What have I done?" he said. "What right have I to spend other people's money in this way? Who do I think I am?"

He thought these thoughts the whole long way back home. As he walked, he worried. The closer he got, the more he more he worried about what he had done. He could not think of how to explain why he had freed those birds instead of buying the seed. He had stolen the money that was entrusted to him to spend. Little by little, he became overwhelmed by his guilt and sorrow. When he came to the last week of his voyage, he could not sleep for his worry. He walked and walked without eating or sleeping. At last, he was so exhausted with his worrying that he fell down and slept a hard sleep.

Out of nowhere, there landed on his chest a beautiful, bright-colored bird. It began to sing a song. It was a pure, clean song—as pure as a kind heart, as unsullied as a generous act.

"Forget your sorrow," sang the bird. "We birds have no gold to repay you. But there are more treasures in the world than gold. We can repay you with the treasures of the birds. Wake and cry no more."

He opened his eyes but the bird had flown off. Or was it a dream? The youth looked around and saw no bird. He heard nothing. He thought it must have been a dream, and once again he began to cry. But then he felt a strong wind. It was a strange wind that he had felt only once before. It was the wind from the wings of the birds he had freed. He looked in the air, and before he could make out any birds they were upon him. All around him in the vast plain the birds stood. They covered the plain like the blades of grass. They were scratching the earth with their claws and dropping something in the holes. They were planting seeds!

The young man moved and suddenly the birds left as quickly as they had come. The hurricane wind of their wings blew through the plain for the last time, and then the birds flew off in their separate ways. The youth was amazed to see that already plants were springing from the earth. Before his eyes, shoots came up and turned into small trees and then into great giant trees weighted down with thick green leaves. As he rubbed his eyes, the youth saw the trees burst out with flowers and fruits of every description.

It was a glorious garden, a splendid garden, a joyous and joyful garden. The youth could not even begin to count the apple trees, the grapevines, the luscious peaches. Thick upon the ground grew luxuriant grass and yellow jonquils nodding in the sun. There were shady paths perfect for a carefree walk. There were clear streams running over beds of bright stones. There were secret clearings. And oak trees. And rowans. All the noble trees and flowers of the earth were there. And in the trees were songbirds that were as sweet-voiced as the bird that sang to the youth when he slept on the plain of despair.

The youth ran as fast as he could to the wise man's hut. When they heard about the Magic Garden, the wise man, Asan, Hasan, and their two children all set out to see it. As they came to the garden, they were pleased with how well the youth had selected his seeds. Then the young man told the story of how he freed the birds and how they had planted the seeds. "You have done well," said the wise man, "for no garden sowed with seed that you bought with gold could have grown so well as this one that was sown by your kindness."

In no time, word spread about the garden. The poor and the needy came to see it. None of them ever had to travel far to find the garden. When they came, they rejoiced in the food and the shelter it gave them. It was a place where the sad and tired could rest and be cheered. It is strange to say that those who did not need the garden, and those who would try to keep the garden for themselves, could never find it. They always found only the garden hedge wall. But when they looked over it they saw nothing at all.

Year after year, the garden was filled, night and day, with the sound of music, laughter, and the singing of the birds.

LESSONS OF THE HEART

It might seem that this story is about good luck since the youth luckily got exactly what he wanted from the money. But he was not just lucky. Had he taken the gold for his own selfish purpose, things would not have gone so well for him. Instead, he acted out of compassion for other living things. When actions are born of such pure motives, they can almost never be the wrong things to do. Thus in the story everything turned out well for the youth, and all the others, "as if by magic."

Story Notes

This is a traditional story from Kazakhstan first encountered by the authors in Mary Masey's *Stories of the Steppes*. It appears as "The Birds' Garden" in *The Gift of the Unicorn and Other Animal Helper Tales* by Dan Keding and Kathleen Brinkman. They in turn give several other sources and classify the story as Motif B450, "Helpful Birds." Other elements of the story, such as two friends trying to force treasure on one another and settling on giving it to the children/couple, can be found in Middle Eastern stories as well, such as "The Land of Peace," available at www.uexpress.com/tell-me-a-story/2014/11/16/the-land-of-peace-a-middle.

THE BEAR CLAN
LEARNS TO HEAL

a woman benefits from her own kindness

Before the world became as it is today, in a time forgotten to living people but remembered in their stories, a group of hunters were running down the trail when they came upon a rabbit. It hopped out right in front of them and just sat there. They shot their arrows at the rabbit. The rabbit made no move, but somehow the arrows missed. The distance was so close that the hunters were sure of a perfect hit. And yet their arrows remained clean. They drew their bows a second time, for the rabbit still sat there waiting. This time as they raised their bows, the rabbit was gone. Instead, on the trail was a frail old man. He seemed to be sick. He asked them for place to rest and some food. The hunters had no time for him and went home to their settlement.

As the old man followed the hunters' path back to the settlement, he grew weaker and weaker. When he arrived in the village, he looked around for a place to rest. In this settlement, the people of the different clans hung outside their dwellings a skin of their particular clan. The stranger thus went from clan to clan seeking help.

As he first entered the village, he stopped at a dwelling where a wolf skin hung. He asked if he might enter and take shelter, for the cold night was coming on. The people inside the wolf house said they would not let him in. They saw a frail, sick stranger at the door. They worried he would bring sickness to them and would be a great burden. They simply told him, "We want no sick man here."

So he staggered as best he could to the next lodging. Outside this one was a turtle's shell. Inside, an old woman of the turtle clan was preparing supper. The shivering old man, sick and ragged, begged her to allow him to come in. She too worried about sickness and didn't want him tracking his mud through her home. She told him to go away.

He tried a home where he saw a beaver skin. A big man standing outside the door saw him coming, and even before the old wanderer could ask the big man said, "Move on, stranger. We don't need your kind around here. You're bad luck, and we want none of that."

Those of the deer clan were just as unkind. The stranger was also chased away from the homes under the signs of the hawk, snipe, and heron.

At last he came to home of the bear clan. Young Orenda [oh-RIN-dah] was cleaning up after supper. Her husband was traveling on a long trip and she was alone for the season. But she was not scared of the stranger, and she was not scared of his illness, and she was willing to bear the burden of his needs.

"Please sir, come in. You look tired," Orenda said.

She made a bed for him and brought him some of what was left of supper.

"You don't look well, elder stranger. I wish that I could help you, but I don't know how."

"Thank you, young lady," said the rabbit man, "and you are right. I am very sick. I suffer greatly in my guts. But do not fear; I know much of healing. I can tell you what to gather and how to prepare it."

And so the old rabbit man told Orenda where to find "five finger root" and how to gather it. She found it quickly and prepared a special tea as he had described. After drinking the tea, the stranger felt much better the next day. But as soon as he got better, he got sick again.

"Goodness, you seem to be sick again," said Orenda.

"Yes, I am sorry to be so much trouble."

"Oh no, do not say that. It is no trouble, except my heart is sad that you suffer so. What can I do to help you?"

"Thank you. I have flu now. But this can be treated with rabbit tobacco."

As before, he described for Orenda how to find the herb and make a special tonic from it. The tonic took a whole day to make, but in the meantime Orenda tended to the man, bringing him food and drink. When the rabbit tobacco tonic was ready, the stranger drank it. The next day his flu was gone, but now he complained of aches and pains.

"I hurt very much, but I can move. I will leave now and will not be a burden any longer."

"Nonsense," said Orenda. "Tell me how to treat this, and you stay here while you get better."

"Ah, well, if you insist, then you should gather arnica, also called 'wolf's bane,' although it is not the same as . . . ."

Again the stranger described to Orenda the herb to gather and how to make a salve out of it so that it could be rubbed on his aches and pains. And so it went, day after day. For the whole season that Orenda's husband was gone, this stranger lay sick, getting almost every illness there was and describing every herb to cure it. Orenda learned the use of dandelion, passion flower, horsemint, milkweed, wild onion, white oak bark, and many other herbs and treatments. Infections, abrasions, disorders, fevers, headaches, and almost any other illness could now be treated by Orenda, thanks to the instructions of the mysterious stranger. Orenda knew more about healing than all the other people put together.

One morning the stranger got up early, and suddenly he seemed very fit and well. He even looked younger.

"I came to his world to teach the people the art of healing," he said. "I went to many a lodging and was turned away. You, alone without help, still let me in because of your kindness. And you, you alone, have learned the ways of healing. You will teach your children, and the bear clan will be honored among the clans for its mastery of the kind art of healing."

Orenda closed her eyes to thank the Great Spirit for sending this messenger. She then turned to thank the man. No one was there, but she saw a rabbit running swiftly down the trail.

Lessons of the Heart

In many tales from many cultures we find the story of hospitality rewarded. Compassion for the stranger is an old and widespread virtue, yet it is not as common in our modern world. This story is especially instructive since it makes the point that the very act of compassion makes us better. In giving of ourselves, we also receive a gift.

Story Notes

This is professed to be a Haudenosaunee legend. A version of it is recorded by Mabel Powers in *Stories the Iroquois Tell Their Children* (New York: American Book Company, 1917). The electronic book is found at Project Gutenberg, www.gutenberg.org/ebooks/22096.

FREEDOM

There's an old saying that "the freedom to swing your fist ends where the tip of my nose begins." In other words, our freedom must always be in balance with the freedom of others.

We wouldn't need to worry about this balance of freedoms if everyone thought the same way, acted the same way, and valued the same things. If everyone was the same, then we wouldn't even need the idea of freedom. We'd simply choose to do what society had already told us to do.

But we aren't all the same. Everyone is different, and we like it this way. As long as we are different, as long as we expect to be allowed to be different, then we have to choose to allow others to be different too. This means we have to value independence and the love of freedom. It means we have to stand up to anything that would crush our own spirit of independence and originality. Without that spirit, we would not be able to reject those who value cruelty and dominance, and we would not be able to act with compassion and justice.

Thus, true freedom requires a strong sense of responsibility. When we are self-indulgent and do whatever we want without regard for how it affects other people, when we ourselves embrace selfishness, cruelty, and dominance, then our freedom is destructive. In other words, when we swing our fist and don't care what we might hit, our freedom is no longer a virtue but a vice.

The wolf learns what freedom truly means.

THE HOUSE DOG AND THE WOLF

Aesop's fable on the price of freedom

Agreat while ago, long before any person can remember, or any animal can remember, or any flower, or tree, or rock can remember, there was a lean and hungry wolf who chanced one night to meet up with a plump, well-fed house dog.

"Tell me, my old friend," said the wolf, "how is it that you look so strong and healthy when there is so little to eat in the forest?"

"As a house dog, I am very well fed."

"I must say the food agrees with you. You are as magnificent a dog as I have seen in many days."

"Thank you, my comrade," said the dog. "But I'll tell you that you can fare as well as I do."

"How? How? Just tell me how and I will do it!" cried the wolf.

"You need only do as I do. All you need to do is guard the master's house and keep away the thieves at night."

"That sounds so nice," the wolf replied. "I have a very hard life in the forest, and the cold and the rain are rough on me now that I am getting older. Oh, to have a roof and food when I like . . . ."

"And in the winter sometimes, there's fire to keep you warm," added the dog.

"How glorious!" said the wolf. "Lead on, my boon companion, lead on."

After they had trotted together for a while, the wolf looked over and saw something shiny on the dog's neck.

"My friend, what is that on your neck?" asked the wolf.

"I'm not sure what you mean. The dark spot in my fur?"

"No, not that," said the wolf. "It is something shiny about your neck like I have never seen in the forest."

"Gee, I cannot imagine what you are talking about unless it's . . . . Oh, but it cannot be that. That's just a trifle."

"What is it?" asked the wolf.

"It's trivial. A nothing. Why, just the collar they use to put the chain on me. You see, I am seen as being rather fierce, and so to be careful they tie me up during the day. Of course, I am at perfect liberty during the night. And master feeds me off his own plate, and I am a favorite with the servants who feed me little tidbits on some days, and— hey, where are you going?"

The wolf said over his shoulder as he ran back to the forest, "You are welcome to your tasty tidbits, but as for me, give me dirt to eat and liberty against a king's feast and a chain."

LESSONS OF THE HEART

All freedom comes at a cost. If we are not willing to give up something—usually a little security—we cannot be free. If we wish to be free, we must stay true to ourselves and make the choice to stay free. Freedom requires that each of us bear a little discomfort. If we cannot do this, we do not deserve to be free.

Story Notes

This is an adaptation of Aesop's "The Wolf and the Housedog." It has been popular for many centuries, and in 1484 it was published in English by William Caxton, the first man to set up a printing press in England.

Box Brown

a story of what a person will risk for freedom

Henry Brown lived a long time ago in the state of Virginia. In those days, there were some places where slavery was not against the law. And in those places, one person could actually own another person as his slave. Not only was the slave not free to do as he wished but it was also against the law for him to escape and for anyone to help him escape. If a slave were caught while trying to escape to freedom, he would be punished harshly and would probably suffer a painful whipping. It was a terrible thing to be a slave, but it was a dangerous thing to try to escape.

Henry Brown was a slave, and like all people he wanted to be free. It was difficult for him simply to run away since his dark skin would reveal that he was a slave. If people saw a man of West African descent traveling across the country by himself, they would get suspicious, and Henry Brown would probably get caught. But he wanted to be free so badly that he was willing to take almost any risk for his freedom. It was while thinking about how he could be free that he hit upon an unusual idea. He decided to build a box. It would be a large box designed so that he could fit inside it along with food, water, and supplies. His plan was to get inside this box and then mail himself to a place where slavery was not allowed.

There were many problems and dangers with Henry Brown's plan. The first was that he needed someplace safe to build the box and he needed wood for the box. Also, after the box was built Henry needed someone to take the box, with him inside, and mail it. Fortunately, Henry was friends with a free man, a handyman and shoe peddler, who thought that slavery was evil. Henry asked this man, James A. Smith, to help him. James Smith agreed to help.

Following Henry Brown's directions James Smith built the box. Once it was finished, they placed inside it the supplies Henry Brown would need on his trip. He had a small bag of water and a couple of biscuits for food. He was given a small hand drill to make holes for air once it was safe for him to do so. He then entered the box, and his friend nailed it shut tight. James Smith addressed the box to some friends who lived in a place where slavery was not allowed. He wrote on the side of the box, "This side up with care."

It might seem to you that there is nothing particularly dangerous about sitting in a box while you go on a trip, but there was a great deal of danger for Henry Brown. It was very hot in the box, and if he got too hot and did not get enough water, and if the trip took too long, then he would die. Also, he was able to get only a little bit of air in the box. If he drilled too many holes, then he would be discovered. This was the other big danger. If Henry Brown said so much as "ouch" or sighed and somebody heard him, then he would be captured and punished. But he felt it was better to risk his life for freedom than live under the cruel hand of slavery. Still, it was no easy trip. It took twenty-six hours for Henry Brown to make his journey. Even though the box was marked "handle with care," it was handled roughly, and Henry received hard knocks, bumps, and bruises. In fact, for miles he had to travel on his head because somebody had placed the box upside down!

When at last Henry Brown arrived, the friends of James A. Smith were waiting for him. In truth, they were afraid that when they opened the box he would be dead. They knew too that if they were caught helping Henry escape, they would be in trouble. Even though slavery was not allowed where they lived, it was still against the law to help a slave escape. So it was some very worried men who came to open the box that contained the brave Henry Brown.

One of the men rapped on the outside of the box and said, "All right?" Right away came back the response, "All right, sir!" Quickly the men got out their tools and opened the box. They never forgot the moment when Henry Brown came out a free man. Rising up out of the box, he was now born into freedom. He reached out his hand and said, "How do you do, gentlemen?" The watchers were all surprised at how well Henry Brown seemed even though he was soaking wet. They were even more surprised when he began to sing:

*I have waited patiently for the Lord, and He inclined
to me and heard my cry.
He drew me up from the desolate pit, out of the miry
bog, and set my feet upon a rock, making my steps
secure.*

He sang this psalm, which he had promised himself he would sing if he arrived into freedom alive. From that day and ever after, in honor of his courage and his creativity and his love of freedom, Henry Brown was no longer called "Henry" by the people who knew him. Instead, he was known as "Box Brown." He settled in his new home and became active in helping other slaves to escape out of bondage.

Box Brown's friend and helper, the handyman James A. Smith, stayed in Virginia. Since the plan worked once, Smith thought that he would try again. This time he tried to mail two slaves to freedom. Unfortunately, he was caught while trying to help these slaves. James A. Smith was arrested and placed in chains. He was taken to a prison where he spent seven years in jail. When he was let out after all those years, he said that he did not feel bad about having to spend this time in jail. He said that he was happy to have struck a blow in the cause of freedom.

Lessons of the Heart

Often we do not appreciate something until we have lost it. Box Brown was a slave who valued freedom so much he took a terrible risk to be free. His friend loved freedom so much that he gave up his own so that others could be free. To maintain our own freedom, we must continue to prize freedom as much as these two men.

Story Notes

Henry "Box" Brown lived from about 1816 until 1897. This tale is based on his true story. Learn more about him from the Virginia Historical Society's article "The Resurrection of Henry 'Box' Brown" at www.vahistorical.org/collections-and-resources/virginia-history-explorer/resurrection-henry-box-brown.

Martin, the Peaceable Soldier

lessons about independence and compassion from a soldier who refused to follow orders

A long time ago, when Rome was still an empire, there lived a boy named Martin. His father was a Roman soldier. This meant that, according to the Roman law, Martin also had to become a soldier. Martin did become a soldier, just like he was supposed to. But he became a soldier who was unlike any other.

Martin was only a teenager when he was ordered into the army like his father. He knew from his father the most important rule for a soldier: you must do what you are told. Martin's father had told him, over and over, ever since he was a young boy, that a soldier's duty is to follow orders. You go where you are told. You go when you are told. And you fight when you are told to fight. Martin understood

that, like his father, like his grandfather, and like every
soldier who ever fought for Rome, he must follow orders
no matter what. So when Martin was ordered away from
his home, he went. He said goodbye to his parents and
was sent off to serve in the far north. It was a long way
from home. Even though Martin had moved around as a
child, because his family followed his father wherever he
was ordered to go, Martin had lived most of his young life
in warm places. But now, for his first posting as a soldier,
he was sent to the cold northern part of France. This was so
long ago that the country wasn't even called "France" yet.
But it was just as cold then as it is now.

About the time that Martin became a soldier, he also
discovered the Christian religion. For many years, Rome
had made it illegal to be a Christian. But by the time
Martin became a soldier, that law had changed. So Martin
had heard about Christians. He became inspired by the one
they called the "Prince of Peace." He decided to become
a Christian himself. In those days, to become a Christian
you didn't just go to church and attend some ceremonies.
You also had to study the teachings of Jesus and the ways of
Jesus. This new young soldier, who was studying to become
a new young Christian, found himself one day on his horse
riding in the cold north. In a snowstorm.

On this day the wind blew cold and the snow fell fast,
and Martin was happy that he was on the way back into
the town where he was stationed. He looked forward to
getting back in quickly and sitting by the barracks fire. As
the son of a horse soldier, Martin too was a horse soldier.

On that day he rode a tall spotted horse. As a horse soldier, he was also given a special long cape. Martin was happy for the warm cape during the storm that day. He wrapped the thick long cape about him. It was especially warm because it covered his whole body. There he was, as a snowstorm was blowing, young teenage Martin riding his horse high above the drifting snow, warm in his long, thick cape. But as he rode along, he saw something. It made him think of what he was learning about being a Christian.

There on the road was a man dressed in rags. He was very poor and shivering. The people who went by ignored him, and when he cried out for help no one paid attention. He was skinny and covered in sores, and no one even wanted to look at him. Martin was high above on his horse and could have easily ridden by. He was just a young soldier, and no one would expect him to help some poor, unimportant beggar. But Martin knew otherwise. He had studied the Christian way. So he took off his cape, took out his sword, and cut his cape in half. He gave half the cape to the old beggar and brought him safely into the town, sharing with him what food he had. Martin did not think about what he had done until that night. As he slept, he had a dream about Jesus, who came to him in the dream clothed in half a cape and saying, "A new Christian has clothed me." From that day on, Martin knew that peace and compassion were his calling as a Christian.

Not long after that, Martin was called to his first battle. The orders went out to the horse soldiers. The next day, they would mount up and ride into battle. They would be fighting and killing for the glory of Rome. They were even allowed to keep any valuable property from the people they defeated if they won. All the soldiers were excited and prepared to follow orders, as the soldiers always did.

But when Martin's captain came to him, Martin said, "I will not fight tomorrow. Men should not kill one another."

Martin's captain was surprised. Here was the son of soldier, who knew how important it was to follow orders but who was refusing to fight. The captain gave him another chance.

"Martin," he said, "you must not understand. This is an order. You are ordered to fight. It is your duty to follow every order without question."

"Captain," said Martin, "I do understand how important orders are. I do understand that my duty as a soldier is to follow every order. But my duty as a Christian is to follow more important orders, and I know that I may not kill. Killing is wrong."

The captain was still surprised. He had Martin arrested. Martin was brought before even more important officers. Every time he was ordered, no matter who gave the order, still Martin refused to fight the next day. Finally, the head general of the army himself confronted Martin.

"Who," said the general, "do you think you are that you can refuse an order? You know that if you refuse to fight, you will be punished for being a coward."

"Yes, I understand," said Martin. "Although I am no one special to refuse orders, I am a follower of the Prince of Peace. I cannot obey your order and also my higher orders.

But I am no coward. You do not have to jail me. You can send me into battle. I will go into battle against the foe who is trying to kill me. But still I will not fight, and I will not take my weapons into battle."

This bewildered the general and all his captains and lieutenants. But after they talked it over a while, they decided that Martin was clearly very brave. So they would not punish him as a coward. Instead, they would allow him to go into battle unarmed. Martin was returned to his captain and to his horse.

The next day, Martin rode in front of the Roman troops, unarmed. The two sides began to fight and then stopped. Before the battle even got started, the two sides had agreed to a peace treaty. They had decided not to fight, so the troops were ordered to lay down their arms, just as Martin had already. No one knows for sure, but some people think that the sight of a brave, unarmed soldier who refused to fight helped the leaders realize how much better it was to work out their disagreements without fighting.

Not long after this, the Roman army decided that Martin would do better work outside the army. He was allowed to leave. Martin then continued his studies as a Christian. He spent the rest of his days traveling and convincing others to join him as a Christian. He helped many people. He taught many people. And he even saved many more people from hardships. He became so popular that people in that part of the world, the country that would someday become France, wanted him to become a church leader called a bishop. But Martin did not want to be tied down to one church. He preferred to live his life wandering and helping people. So a group of people came up with a trick. They spread the word about many sick and hungry people who needed help. When Martin arrived to help, as he always did, everyone around came to him. They shouted and begged and pleaded and cried and made such a fuss that, just to keep the peace and quiet, Martin agreed to become a bishop. He lived many years as a holy man, helping people until he grew old. The people of the country that would become France loved him very much. When he died, they picked the day of his death to be a day for a special feast. And when France became a country, the French chose Saint Martin as the protector of France and the special protector of soldiers. Long after Martin's death, soldiers have prayed to Saint Martin, asking for his protection.

So it went for many years. For more than one thousand five hundred years the people of France looked to Martin, and so too the soldiers of France. Then France got into a terrible war with its neighbor, Germany. It was the worst war France had ever seen. Many people suffered, and many people died. The French countryside had never seen such death; the French had never known so much sorrow. For four long years France struggled in this terrible war. The beautiful green grasses growing in the countryside, the same hills and valleys wandered by Saint Martin, now were wet with tears and blood. After four long years, finally the day of peace came. It was a blessing and a joy to the people of France. And it just so happens that the exact day when

France and Germany agreed to stop fighting was the feast day of Saint Martin.

Maybe it was just a coincidence that the terrible war ended on Saint Martin Day. But some people do not think this was an accident. Some people say that Saint Martin was at last remembered by those who had been fighting, and that once again he had stopped a war. Whatever you think, it is nice to remember on Veteran's Day, on November 11, that this is also Saint Martin Day. It is the day of the saint who watches after soldiers. The saint who teaches us that peace is better than war. The man who proved that the most important freedom we can fight for is the freedom to follow the orders of our hearts even if this means sometimes disobeying the orders of the world.

LESSONS OF THE HEART

Saint Martin is the patron saint of soldiers, conscientious objectors, and tailors! Sadly, he is forgotten by many people in America these days. While we justly celebrate soldiers on November 11, Saint Martin reminds us that celebrating soldiers is not the same thing as celebrating killing. Saint Martin showed many virtues of the heart, including compassion and courage. But above all, he showed the virtue of independence, of freedom. He did not let others tell him what to do, and he did not let the rules set down by an emperor tell him how to act. He made up his own mind based on his own

*understanding of what was the right thing to do, and
he insisted on the freedom to follow his own conscience.*

Story Notes

This tale is based on the true story of Saint Martin of Tours. A figure
as iconic as this one, of course, has many legends, and various versions
of the basic facts of his life can be found in many online sources.

Jack, Jill, and the Great Glowing Beast

a story of how the truth can set you free

Far, far away, and very much longer ago, in the days when animals could talk, there lived Jack the bunny and also bunny Jill. Jack and Jill were born the same day, the same hour, and the same litter to the same momma, who was Jay-Jay.

Even when he was young, Jack had the greatest and longest feet of all the rabbits in all the warrens of the long-ago times. He was proud of his feet and what he could do with his feet. Always he said, "Just look at these feet. They are marvelous feet, for they can leap higher than any other feet, and they can hop farther than all the hopping of all those other feet." But as magnificent as Jack's feet were, Jill too was magnificent. For Jill had the greatest and longest legs of all the rabbits in all the warrens of the long-ago times.

Always Jill said, "Just look at my legs. They are wondrous legs, for they can run swifter than any other legs, and they can zig quicker and zag faster than all the ziggy-zaggy legs of all the beasts who run through the dark forests and race through the green meadows." So Jack and Jill would spend their days in leaping and spend their days in running. They ended their days when Jack would hippity-hop into bed and Jill would ziggity-zag under her covers. They were almost perfectly happy living this way and almost never thought of anything but running and hopping and laughing for joy.

Jay-Jay, their mother, worried about Jack, for Jack would never listen when lessons were given; instead, he would think about hopping and dream about leaping. So also Jay-Jay also worried about Jill since Jill never paid attention when lessons were given, but instead she would think about zigging and dream about zagging. Jay-Jay tried to tell them that if they were to get by in the world, then they must learn from their lessons. But Jack and Jill would say, "Why do we have to learn? We have Jack's feet and Jill's legs." Jay-Jay would tell them of all the things they must know if they were to grow up and someday have little rabbit kits themselves. For as it is now for the rabbits, so it was too in the long-ago times. T he world was full of the enemies of the rabbits, and rabbits had to know the secrets of the world so that they could escape with the clever and tricksey, witty and sneaksey ways of the rabbit. But when Jay-Jay would tell them this, always Jack would say, "Why should I be tricksey? If I see coyote, I will shake my big and magnificent feet and leap over coyote, and I will hippity-hop on his head and jump far away before he can catch me!" So Jill too would always say, "Why should I be sneaksey? If owl swoops down for me, I will twist zig zig zig, and I will turn zag zag zag, and I will run far away before she can grab me!" No matter how much Jay-Jay told them that feet and legs are not enough, still Jack would never listen, and still Jill would never pay attention. Even though everyone else called Jack "Jack-Big-Foot," his mother called him "Jack-Who-Never-Learns." And even though everyone else called Jill "Jill-Strong-Leg," her mother Jay-Jay called her "Jill-Who-Never-Listens."

The only thing Jack liked as much as his feet was the beautiful white nose of his sister. It was white as the stars, as the hail, as the foam that flowed from the rivers and streams in the mountains of the long-ago times. The only things Jill liked as much as her legs were the beautiful long ears of her brother. Jack's ears were floppy and flippy and colored like lavender and raindrops painted together in broad, bright stripes. "Oh, how I wish," Jack would say, "that you could see how perfectly white your nose is, sister." And Jill would reply, "No less do I wish, brother, that you could see how gloriously striped your ears are." The only thing that kept Jack from being perfectly happy was the thought that he could not see his ears, and Jill also thought that if she could see her nose, then she would at last be perfectly happy. So one day, they decided that they would go to the lake in the old tall forest where the water is still and the water is shiny, so still and shiny that if you looked in it you could see your own face looking back at you. They said to one another,

"We will go to the forest lake and we will see our own faces looking back at us, and Jack will see his ears, and Jill will see her nose, and we will be perfectly happy." But even in the long-ago times, perfect happiness was not an easy thing to find.

When Jack and Jill told their mother of their plan to go to the forest lake and see their own faces looking back at them, Jay-Jay told them they could go but that they should make sure to stay on the broad straight road that led to the lake. Also she said to them, "If you come home after dark you can hurry along by the light of the moon, and that way you can see to stay on the road. You have never seen the moon because we are always in our holes at night. The moon is a big friendly light like the sun but not so bright. Its light is soft like the soft furry patches on your soft bunny chests and will help you along. It has dark patches and light patches that look like a great face, but do not worry. It is just a gentle, friendly light. Come quickly in the moonlight and do not dawdle, for I will worry if you miss your bedtime." But once Jay-Jay told them that they could go, and how they could get there by the broad straight road, Jack no longer listened to what she said, and Jill no longer paid attention. So they did not notice what their mother told them about the moon.

The next day, Jay-Jay packed for her two kits a carrot for their lunch, some lettuce and a radish for their supper, and sent them on their way. She kissed each one right between the ears and over the nose, and reminded them that as long as they stayed on the broad straight road and came straight home after they saw the lake, then all would be well. Jack kissed his momma, told her they would stay on the road, and hippity hopped on down the road. Jill also kissed her momma and promised, and right alongside Jack she zigged and zagged on down the road.

They ran and they jumped out of their warren and went down the broad straight road. Down the road and through the rocky hills they ran. Down the road and through the grassy meadows they jumped. They ran and jumped until at last the road took them into the old tall forest. The wind blew in the forest, in the high branches, bringing air from faraway places whose secrets are whispered by the wind. The wind knew secrets Jack and Jill would never know and had seen places they would never see, and still it was right there, blowing through the forest in the high branches. Under the trees, under the wind, under the secrets Jack hopped and Jill raced, down the broad straight road, until they came at last to the lake of the forest.

It was lunchtime when Jack and Jill came to the deep and shiny lake in the middle of the forest. Jack was hungry but so excited to see his ears that he rushed to the lake before eating his carrot. Jill also was too excited to eat, and she rushed over to the lake so she could see her pure white nose. As they ran they said, "By long bunny legs and by strong bunny feet, now we can be perfectly happy!" When Jack looked into the lake he saw his beautiful ears, and this made him very pleased. Jill felt pleased too when she saw a face with a pure white nose looking back at her from the lake. But, pleased as they were, somehow neither Jack nor Jill felt as perfectly, wonderfully happy as they thought they would be. They stayed a long time staring at their own faces looking back at them and slowly began to wonder if maybe it might take more than strong limbs and good-looking faces to be perfectly happy. Then they thought of their carrots and sat down to eat.

"Maybe," said Jack as he munched on his carrot, "it will take more than just seeing our faces to make us perfectly happy."

"Maybe," said Jill, "you are right."

When their thinking and their munching and their carrots were all finished, Jack and Jill headed for home. They remembered to stay on the broad straight road and they remembered that they must get home before bedtime or else Jay-Jay would be worried. But they did not remember about the moon because they had not listened or learned when Jay-Jay gave that lesson.

They got back on the road, said good-bye to the deep still lake, and headed back home. It was a long way home, and by the time Jack and Jill left the forest and came upon a broad open field it was getting dark and time for supper. But just as Jack began to eat his radish and Jill began to nibble on her lettuce, they saw something that scared them so much; it was so huge and bright and white that it made them stop chewing with the radish and the lettuce still in their mouths.

"Wat is dat?" said Jack with his mouth full of radish.

"I dunno!" said Jill with her mouth full of lettuce.

For a few spooky moments, Jack and Jill sat there staring at the giant glowing thing in the sky. It seemed to have face in it. It reminded them of something they had heard about. Something scary.

"It has the big glowing eyes of the coyote that Momma Jay-Jay talked about one time," said Jack, who had not paid much attention so he didn't really know what a coyote looked like.

"It has the bright unblinking eye of the owls that Momma Jay-Jay talked about one time," said Jill, who hadn't listened and didn't really know much about owls.

The longer they sat, the longer they thought the great glowing eyes of the huge face were staring right at them, and the more frightened they became. Then, far away, deep in the forest, a bird landed on a high branch, and a pine-cone, almost as big as a rabbit kit, was knocked off and fell a long way down, landing with a thud so loud that, far away in the meadow, two kits with good rabbit hearing and huge rabbit ears heard the thump and got scared.

"It's coming!" they shouted together, and both at once sprang into action.

First, Jack said, "We do not need to be afraid; I will leap over the great glowing beast!"

But as high as Jack leaped and as long as he jumped and as far far far as he hopped, he could not jump over the great glowing face.

Then Jill said, "We do not need to be afraid; I will run so that the great glowing beast cannot follow!"

But no matter how fast Jill ran, how sudden she zigged, or how sharply she zagged, when she looked behind her there it was still—the great glowing face.

Now that Jack's feet and Jill's legs had failed them, the young bunny siblings were very much afraid indeed.

"Oh, what can we do?" they cried. "We do not know any sneaky tricks. What can we do?"

And as they cried, they remembered the first trick any bunny learns, the first and only trick they knew about. They must hide. They looked to the left and saw only grass that would not hide them well. They looked to the right and saw only flowers that were too short to hide behind. Then they looked all around and saw up ahead a gnarly, tangled, dense bramble bush.

"If we can get there we can hide," they said to each other. So in no time they were at the bramble, and all the while the great glowing beast was right behind them. Jack pushed his face into the bramble bush, and the sticks and thorns poked at him and scratched his striped ears. Jill's face too was poked, and her white nose was scratched by brambles and thorns. But they didn't worry about that now; they pushed through as Jack ears got scratched and Jill's nose got cut, and they found a small place to hide. In the middle of the bramble bush was a small opening just big enough for the two bunny kits. It was very uncomfortable, with no room to move. But it was out of sight of the great glowing beast.

"We will hide here, and then we can move on later," they whispered, now too scared even to talk out loud. There they sat, all cramped up like prisoners in the bramble bush. Every now and then one of them would whisper, "Is the beast still there?" Then they would poke through the brambles and the thorns, cutting their faces, getting pokes in their soft bunny bellies and in their pink bunny eyes. But all night long, whenever they looked out, there it was—the great glowing beast. When morning came they wanted to check again. But Jack said to Jill, "You go. I am all scratched and cut, and I am too tired." Then Jill said to Jack, "No, you go. I am tired and full of little cuts. I just want to sleep." So all day long, they stayed imprisoned in that little place, cramped together and trying to sleep. Whenever Jack would stretch he would poke Jill, who would say, "Ow, ow, ow! Be careful." And when Jill would roll over she would crush Jack who would say, "Ouch! Watch out." So they spent all day too tired to move, too uncomfortable to get much sleep.

That night they finally decided they could look and see if it was safe to move. They fought past the thorns and the sticks and the sharp brambles and looked out. When they did, their hearts dropped in their bunny chests, and tears came to their bunny eyes. There floated the great glowing beast looking down on them. They clawed their way back to the little cramped opening and cried. "We are trapped. We cannot move or the great glowing beast will get us. We have no food, and we cannot sleep. What will we do? We are not free to go, but we also cannot stay."

Now bedtime had come and bedtime had gone. Then breakfast, then lunch, then supper had all come and gone.

It was almost bedtime again, and down the broad straight road came Jay-Jay looking for her lost kits. It so happened that just as Jack and Jill cried out about how they were prisoners in the bramble bush jail, Jay-Jay was hopping by. When she heard them, all the worry that had sat on her heart like a great ugly toad turned to joy, just like an ugly toad that is given a loving kiss turns into a beautiful golden child.

Jay-Jay cried out to her kits, "Jack and Jill, Jill and Jack, where are you? Come out so I can see you." Then she heard from inside the bramble bush her kits crying to her: "Oh, Momma, we are too afraid to come out. We are hiding from the great glowing beast."

Jay-Jay followed the sound of her kits' voices. She stood outside the brambles and told them there was nothing to fear, no great glowing beast. As the two young rabbits cried and trembled, they described for her the great round glowing face that no one could jump over, that no one could outrun, and that hung high in the sky all night and watched for them. Jay-Jay had to laugh.

"You silly bunnies! I know what you mean. That is the moon I told you about. It's a friendly light, like the sun, but it comes out at night and shines with silver light instead of yellow. The moon will not harm you. The moon can never harm you. The moon never was going to harm you. There is no great glowing beast."

Jack and Jill could not believe how lucky they were, and it was a happy and joyful Jay-Jay who pushed aside the branches and rescued her little kits from the bramble bush prison. Jack was covered with scrapes and dirt, and his ears were such a shambles you could hardly see the stripes. Jill had many tiny cuts and bruises, and her nose was smeared with mud where she had hidden her face in the ground. Jay-Jay hugged and kissed her little kits, and all together they hopped on home.

For the whole next week, Jay-Jay spoiled them and patted them and fed them their favorite food. She licked their wounds and kissed their bruises, but still, as sorry as she felt for them, she gave them their lessons in between her kisses.

"All that time, you were free but didn't know it. All that time, only your own fear of what you didn't understand kept you imprisoned. Your jail keeper was your own fear, and the jail was your own ignorance. No jailer is as watchful as the fear in your own heart, and no jail is as cruel as a mind that will not learn."

Jack and Jill tried to understand, and they decided that if they were to stay free, if they were ever to find perfect happiness, then maybe they should change their ways. So Jack was no longer Jack-Who-Never-Learns, and Jill was no longer Jill-Who-Never-Listens. From then on, they tried to learn and pay attention. They learned a lot and were never again kept prisoner by their own ignorance and fear.

LESSONS OF THE HEART

From Jack and Jill we learn that freedom from needless fear is the most important freedom of all. When we are too fearful to act according to our true nature, then we find that we cannot fulfill our potential. We become prisoners to our anxiety. And there is no better antidote to fear than knowledge. As the saying goes, "The truth will set you free."

Story Notes

This is an original story. The idea for it came from the Hindu notion of a man who sees a rope in dim light and, not recognizing it as a rope, is fearful of a snake. Only the truth of the light releases him from the paralysis of fear.

RESPECT

Like the other virtues, respect can be simple and complicated at the same time. Basically, respect is the recognition that every single person on earth is a member of humanity and must be treated as a person and not a thing. Respect is based on the very idea that all people are created equal.

We all know that, don't we? But what about the people we don't like? Yes, they still deserve our respect. Our dislike of them does not make them any less human.

What about the people we would judge and punish? Do we have to treat them as equal members of humanity? Strange as it seems, the act of punishment itself acknowledges that the wrongdoer is still a person and is responsible for his or her actions and must be taught to do better.

It is important to realize that prejudice and foolish pride are the enemies of respect. We are wrong if we prejudge others based on how they seem at first.

We have learned nothing about virtue if we can convince ourselves that there are people who can be totally ignored because they do not deserve our basic respect.

Hodja shows that people sometimes respect the wrong thing.

EAT, COAT, EAT

a farmer with a fine coat
teaches his friend about respect

Did you ever hear the story of Hodja [ha-JEE] and his hungry coat? You have not? Good! That means I will tell it to thee. And once you know it, then you can tell it to me.

It was the day of Halil's [hah-LEEL] party. Everyone was invited. Certainly his good friend Hodja was expected to come as an important guest.

But, party or not, the day was a working day for Hodja. He had his garden to harvest and his vegetables to take into town. All morning he loaded his crops onto his cart, and then he made the dusty trip into town to sell them. When he was done, he turned for home. Whenever he took his crop into town, Hodja would get his clothes dirty from the digging and from the road. So he always wore his plain working clothes on working days. This meant that on the day of Halil's big party, Hodja found himself in town, dressed in his plain everyday clothes. Instead of going directly to Halil's house there in town, Hodja instead headed back to his farmhouse so he could clean up and put on his nice coat.

As he headed on the homeward road, Hodja passed one person and then another coming the other way. All were dressed in their finery, and all were on their way to Halil's party. "Hello, Hodja," they would say, "you are going the wrong way if you want to feast with Halil tonight."

"I am just going to clean up and get changed," said Hodja.

"Well, hurry if you want to have anything left. You don't want Halil to think you don't care to be there."

It wasn't too long before Hodja realized, even as he hurried, that the sun was almost down; if he took the time to wash and dress, he would be too late for the banquet.

"I must go as I am," he thought. "If it were anyone but my friend Halil, I should be worried to show up like this. But Halil and I have seen many long years together. No need to fret."

He turned his donkey around and headed back into town, toward the house of his friend. When he got to Halil's, he tied up his donkey and then walked without any worry at all into the house where the feast was in preparation. He was sure that he would get a big welcome, and so he spoke in his usual easy manner with everyone he met. He smiled at each person and told jokes left and right. He thought he was being his usual charming self, but he noticed something strange. No one was laughing. No one was even answering him. In fact, nobody was looking him in the face. As soon as he saw a face, it was gone and he was talking to the back of someone's head. Stranger still, when the soup course was announced Halil welcomed all the others by name but had nothing to say to Hodja.

"Ahem," Hodja began, clearing his throat.

Halil did not notice.

Hodja coughed loudly.

Halil paid no attention.

"Oh, Halil," Hodja said in a loud voice, "you have the finest home in all the great valley."

Still Halil seemed unable to hear or see his guest, who stood alone in his scruffy work clothes.

Hodja looked at the others. They were each dressed in their best clothes, cleaned with a sheen and perfumed to sweet-smelling perfection. Then Hodja looked at his brown hands caked with the dust of a hard day's work. He looked at his clothes with patches over the rips caused by toil and with stains from the sweat of his labor.

Very quietly Hodja slipped out of the house, collected his donkey, and headed for home.

Once home he quickly took a bath with the finest soaps and oils. Getting dressed, he called to his servants.

"Hurry. My best turban. My new coat. Quickly."

His servants brought him the coat his wife had bought him for special occasions. It was his "once-a-year coat," embroidered by skilled artisans with threads of gold and silver. Jewels were sewn to the cuffs, and the most delicate and complex designs a mind could devise were woven into its fiber.

What an impressive sight he made now! As he swaggered back along the street, the onlookers stopped and admired him. Little boys bowed to him as he passed, shopkeepers called him "Effendi" (or "sir") as they beckoned him to come see their wares, and young ladies secretly peeked at him from behind their veils, too shy to speak.

Once at Halil's, he was received in grand style. A servant ushered him into the dining room. Halil himself greeted Hodja warmly with a broad smile. Halil piled Hodja's plate with wonderful foods of all description. All the guests sought out Hodja and wanted him to show them the honor of paying attention to them. They told him their best stories and jokes, and everyone was as friendly as Hodja could hope.

Once he knew he was the center of attention, Hodja started his lesson.

Taking the choicest delicacy from his plate, he raised it not to his lips but to his coat. As his surprised admirers looked on, he put the food in his coat pocket and said, "Eat, coat, eat."

One delicacy after another—figs, dates, lamb, raisins, and yogurt—made its way into his pocket. With each morsel he said for all to hear, "Eat, coat, eat."

The conversation stopped. The eating stopped. The whole party stopped just so the people could watch this curious spectacle. Finally, Halil, whose party was quickly being ruined, could stand it no more and asked, "Hodja, are you crazy? Why are you shoving food into your good coat? You are ruining the coat and wasting the food. And above all, why on earth do you tell your coat to eat?"

"Why, I just figured that you would want my coat to eat." Then Hodja fixed his gaze upon Halil. "When I came in my old clothes, you did not even sit me at the table or treat me like someone who belonged at the banquet. But when I come in my fancy clothes, everything is changed. Now I am offered every comfort and delicacy and am treated like a special guest. That shows it was the coat, not me, that you invited to your banquet."

LESSONS OF THE HEART

It is said that the clothes make the person, but Hodja shows that we must respect people rather than clothes. Respect is owed to people as people and not for who they are in society. We earn respect by our humanity, not by wearing a fancy coat.

Story Notes

This story is adapted from an Islamic folk tale that can be found in several different countries, including Turkey and Syria. In Turkey the main character is known as Nasruddin Hodja, and there are many tales about him. "Effendi" is an address of honor meaning, roughly, "sir."

THE FAIRIES

a French fairytale about respect

Once upon a time, when the world was full of wonders, there was a widow who had two daughters. The elder daughter, Greta, was just like her mother in temperament and looks. Both were so haughty and self-satisfied that no one could stand them. The younger daughter, Claire, was gentle and good-natured. The mother doted on her older daughter but treated the younger one poorly. She made her eat in the kitchen and work like she was a servant rather than a member of the family.

One of Claire's jobs was to go twice a day to fetch water. To do this, she had to travel for miles with a big jug. Even so, she never complained. One day when she was at the fountain to get water, a poor woman came up to her and begged her for a drink. "Of course," said the kind girl. She rinsed her jug and filled it with fresh water. She then offered water to the old woman. She held up the heavy jug for the old woman in order to make it easier for her to drink. Once the woman finished, Claire had to lift the heavy jug back down to the fountain and fill it again.

"You have such a kind heart that it makes you very beautiful," said the old woman, "and it makes me want to give you a gift."

"Oh no," said the girl. "Please, it is not necessary."

But the woman insisted. What Claire did not know was that the old woman was a water fairy who guarded the fountain. This fairy had taken the form of an old woman as a test of kindness.

"The gift that I give you," said the fairy as she waved her arms over her head, "is that each time you speak, a flower or a precious gem will fall from your mouth."

As the girl began to ask questions about what the fairy had done, two peonies and a sapphire fell out of her mouth. Before the startled girl could react, the fairy was gone.

Claire hefted her water jug and trudged home. As soon as she got home, her mother began to scold her for taking so long at the fountain.

"I am so sorry, Mother, for being late," said the girl. As she spoke, two roses and two pearls fell out of her mouth.

"What's this?" said her mother. "Are those pearls? How can that be? What has happened to you, my darling?" Her mother spoke to her in a kind voice for the first time in a very long time.

Claire innocently told her mother what had happened at the fountain—how she had been kind and, as a reward, the fairy cast this spell on her. As she told the story, even more flowers and gems fell from her mouth.

"Very interesting," said the mother. "I must send my good daughter."

She called to her older daughter. "Greta, take a look at your sister. See how many fine things she has just by talking. Wouldn't you like the same thing to happen to you? All you have to do is go to this fountain and fetch water. When a poor old woman asks you for a drink give her one, but be sure to be polite and kind."

"Oh, just try to get me to go to the fountain! That's a servant's work. I won't do it," replied Greta.

Now her mother stormed over to Greta. "You must go right away!" insisted her mother.

So off went Greta, grumbling all the way. She took the best silver flask in the house. It was much smaller and easier to carry than the old jug her sister had carried. When she reached the fountain, she saw a small, helpless child.

"Please, miss," said the child. "I cannot reach the fountain and I am so thirsty. Could I have a drink?"

This was the very same fairy who had appeared to Claire, but now she came as a young child rather than an old woman. Again she was testing the kindness of those who came to her fountain.

"Do you think I came all this way to serve you water? Besides, you are so dirty you would ruin my fine pitcher. Go find someone else to serve you. Leave me alone, you brat!"

"You are not very kind," replied the fairy child calmly. "Because you are so mean and ill-spoken, I will give you a special gift."

The child waved her hands and a loud clap came from the sky. As simple as that, Greta got the gift she had earned.

As soon as Greta came within sight of her home, her mother rushed out to see her.

"Well, Greta? What happened? What happened?"

"Mother . . . ," Greta began.

But as she spoke, her mother jumped back in fear. Out of rude Greta's mouth flew a toad and a snake. Her mother was horrified, but, as usual, she blamed the younger sister. She ran after Claire, trying to beat her and crying, "Why have you done this to my beloved Greta?" Her mother was so angry that the younger daughter was afraid to stay. She ran away into the next town. With her gems and flowers and kindness, she was treated very well and chose to settle there. She used her gems as wisely as her words and grew to old age well loved and happy. Meanwhile, her mother and older sister spoke so many mean and spiteful things to one another that it was not long until their whole house was overrun by snakes and toads and ugliness.

LESSONS OF THE HEART

Respect is born spontaneously from our regard for others. It is not simply an attempt to impress others with our good manners. When we recognize the value of others, we are naturally respectful to them without even thinking about it. Good manners are good only as long as they are born of true respect and not just

*habit. The virtue of respect eludes us whenever we seek
a reward for being respectful.*

Story Notes

This is a retelling of a story from the famous *Perrault's Fairy Tales*,
first published in 1697.

THE WOODEN BOWL

*a tale about many things, including how those
who seek respect must show it to others*

In a certain realm in a certain land in a certain village,
Karl was born. And it seemed that, almost as fast as you
could turn around, Karl became a young man. In those
days, in that realm, it was the custom for a youth to go out
into the world and seek to make his life as best he could.

So Karl kissed his mother, hugged his father, and,
with a tear in his eye, walked down the road. It wasn't too
long before Karl found a job with a farmer. He worked
and he saved, he saved and he worked, and he dreamed
about buying his own farm someday. After a while he met
young Maria, and they got married. Maria too got a job,
and together they worked, together they saved, and they
cared for one another, doing the best they could.

After so much working and saving, Karl and Maria
bought a farm. But of course, this did not end their

working. Now they worked even more. They raised cows, they grew corn, and they tended gardens. And sometimes the winds blew the crops away. Sometimes their cows took sick. Sometimes raccoons raided the gardens all dressed in their raccoon burglar masks, stealing away on clever raccoon feet. Many things threatened the happiness of Karl and Maria, but they didn't care. All that mattered to them was their love, and so when trouble came they took a deep breath, rolled up their sleeves, and continued to do the best they could.

It wasn't long—it seemed like only a few moments— before Karl and Maria had their first child—a boy. They named him Hans. After Hans came three more children. And quicker than a squirrel can disappear from sight, the farm was filled with livestock and with crops and with the sound of children's laughter. When Hans grew old enough, Karl and Maria showed him how to raise crops and tend animals and help around the home. As the other children grew older, each in turn learned to help as well. All together, the whole family cared for their farm, and they cared for one another.

It wasn't long, no longer than it takes to dance a Saturday morning jig, before Hans grew up and left home. Like Karl, he kissed his mother, hugged his father, and off he went. In turn, each of the children also grew up and left home. As quick as that, Karl and Maria were left to run their farm again, together and alone. But now they had grown old—yes, swiftly the years had flowed away, still it was long years that had passed. Karl had become an old man and Maria an old woman. And in their old age they loved one another and their farm, were proud of their children, and so were happy. For just a while longer, they were happy together. In the fullness of time, the day came, as such days do, that they were parted. Maria passed on and then Karl was alone again.

But now Karl was so old that he had trouble keeping up his farm, and he had trouble dealing with being all alone. He tried and he tried, yes, he did the best he could, but he could no longer make it without some help. So the day came, so much quicker than it should have, when Karl sold his farm and moved in with Hans, his wife, Hilda, and their child, Karl's grandson Max.

At first Karl helped around the young couple's farm because he did not want to be a burden. But Karl was so old now that there wasn't much he could do. He fed the chickens and even swept the floor, but he was not very good at any kind of physical work anymore. Even with easy work, his hands would shake and his knees would tremble. He was happiest when they had him look after young Max, which was no trouble when Max was just a baby. And when Max got older, Karl loved to tell him stories of the times he knew and the people he had known and the silly things Hans had done when he was a boy. Max looked forward to the stories, but, like all kids, Max didn't always just sit still and listen. Sometimes he wanted to run and play, and sometimes he was stubborn, wouldn't do what he was told, and could be a real handful. So in the end, even watching Max became too much for old Karl. Still, he did whatever was asked of him; he tried, anyway, because he didn't want to be a burden.

Time went on, and old Karl became even older and feebler. In those days, in that realm, they didn't have medicines like we have now, so all the ailments and sicknesses suffered by Karl never got any better but just got worse and worse. His hands began to shake more, his grip became weak, his legs became unsteady, and he even started to forget the stories he tried to tell Max. When he sat at the dinner table, he could barely hold his spoon. Often he would spill his food on the tablecloth, and sometimes his soup would spill back out of his mouth. Hans and Hilda were disgusted by the sight of old Karl eating with them, so they decided they would have him sit away from the rest of the family and feed him at a table in the corner of the room. When they told Karl this, he said nothing but took the change the same as when the wind blew away his crops and when time at last took Maria. He loved his family very much, so if this was what they wanted, then he would do this for them. Sometimes, it is true, his eyes grew a little wet while he was eating, but otherwise he tried to accept the change and meet the challenge, like he always did.

It went this way for several months: old Karl was forced sit apart from the others so that no one had to look at him while he ate. He missed having dinner like a real person, like a member of the family, but he appreciated having food to eat. No matter what, he was grateful for what he had. One day his hands were shaking worse than ever. He was having soup for supper, and he held the bowl in his hand so that he wouldn't have so far to go with the spoon. Then his hands shook again and the bowl fell on the ground and broke. Soup and glass were all over the floor. Hans and Hilda were very upset. They started scolding him; yes, Karl's own son scolded him as if Karl was a little child.

"Just look what you've done!" said Hans, "We can't give you anything nice or you ruin it. You got stains all over our tablecloth, and now you break one of our bowls. It was a matched set! I guess you just can't have nice things."

Then Hans and Hilda decided they would make Karl eat with a bowl that could not be broken. All they had was an ugly old wooden bowl they used to mix up the dog's food. They cleaned this out and gave it to Karl.

"There," said Hans, feeling a little guilty, "do not be worried. It is a nice, clean bowl now, and sturdy too. You will never break this bowl."

Karl smiled at his son and made no complaint. Karl was not one who complained. He loved his son, and for him he would do the best he could.

It went this way for several more weeks, the mother and father and son at one table eating like people, and the old grandfather at another table eating like something less than a person. So it went until the youngest member in the family did something very wise, even though he did not know how wise it was.

One day by the fire Max took a bit of iron and a piece of wood. He scraped on the wood in the middle and started to make a dent, then a ditch, then what looked like a bowl. His father, Hans, watched this for a while. Hans was pleased with Max's patience and his determination to hollow out the wood with just a scrap of metal.

"Well, son," said Hans, "that's quite a work you have going there. What are you making?"

"I am making a wooden bowl," said Max.

"Oh? Is that so?" said Hans, amused. "It's a fine little bowl, but aren't you happy with the good glass bowl you eat out of? The one with the nice pattern and the smooth, deep curve?"

"This bowl isn't for me," said Max.

"No? Then why are you trying to make that funny little bowl out of wood?" asked Karl.

"It's for you and Mama so that when you are old and your hands tremble like grandfather's, you'll have something to eat out of," replied Max.

Hans and Hilda looked at one another. Suddenly they realized what they had been doing. They thought about how they would feel if they were forced to eat that way, and all at once they understood how disrespectful they had been. They knew what they had done was wrong. They knew that tablecloths and fancy bowls and a little unpleasantness were nothing compared to the respect and love they owed old Karl.

They brought Karl back to the big table. They told him they were sorry and promised to show him the respect he deserved. This made Karl happy, for it was all he needed to be happy—to have some respect from those he loved. Karl ate at the family table for all the rest of his days. And if his hands shook or food spilled out of his mouth, no one worried too much about it. So it was in this way that they—all of them together—did the best they could.

LESSONS OF THE HEART

In this story we learn several lessons about respect. Fundamentally, Hans and Hilda come to realize that love without respect is hollow sentiment. Also, Max teaches them that respect is a two-way street, and those who live disrespectfully cannot expect others to respect them.

Story Notes

This story is so common on the Internet that the authors originally thought it was an example of an Internet-created folk tale. But actually it can be found in the 1857 edition of *Grimm's Fairy Tales* as story #78, "The Old Grandfather and His Grandson." The Brothers Grimm collected what in German they called "Hausmärchen," meaning household fairy tales—the sort told around the kitchen table. The Snopes page www.snopes.com/glurge/woodbowl.asp discusses the phenomenon of this story's frequent appearance in emails and blogs. Clearly the Internet has changed only the size of the kitchen table and not necessarily the type of stories we like to tell.

JIMMY AND THE WAMPUS CAT

a story about outcasts and the respect they earn

B ack before your time, back before my time, before the time of your grandmothers and grandfathers, before they had doohickeys and gizmos and computers and cell phones and digital cameras, way back in the back-before times, which is to say, once upon a time in the deep dark pine woods of Mississippi, a mountain lion gave birth to three cubs. Two of the baby lions were golden brown just like mountain lion cubs are supposed to be. But to the mother lion's surprise, one of the cubs was white as snow.

"This is very strange," said all the other mountain lions. "Cubs are supposed to be brown."

One of the nosy mountain lions said to the mother, "I don't know what you're going to do with that strange white cub."

The mother lion just smiled and licked the little white cub and said, "I'm gonna love him just like I love my other cubs." And she licked and licked him, and the little cub felt warm and safe snuggled up to his mother.

But as the white cub got older, he began to notice that he was different from the other mountain lions. He noticed that the other young cubs looked at him strangely and did not want to play with him. Later on, when the young lions were beginning to roar their loud and scary roar, the white lion discovered his voice was different. No matter how hard he tried, his roar came out like a high shriek. It made all the other lions laugh. He was white, *and* he couldn't roar. Some of the other lions pointed to him and said, "He doesn't sound like a mountain lion, and he doesn't look like a mountain lion. He's not a real mountain lion."

Sometimes it made the white lion cry, so he began to play by himself. That way he would not have to listen to the laughter and the unkind words of the other lions. As he walked through the woods, other animals and birds pointed at him and talked about him. They had never seen such a different-looking creature.

"Is it some kind of cat?" the field mouse asked the wise owl. The field mouse was always on the lookout for cats.

"Well," said the owl, "I wouldn't say 'yes' and I wouldn't say 'no.' I'd be afraid to say."

"Is it some kind of dog?" the rabbit asked the wise owl. The rabbit had been chased by many a dog, and he was always on the lookout for dogs.

"Well," said the owl, "I wouldn't say 'yes' and I wouldn't say 'no.' I'd be afraid to say."

And several other animals asked the owl, "What do you think it is?"

The owl scratched his head and thought for a long time, and then he answered, "Sometimes I think . . . well, then again I just don't know."

So all the animals stayed away from the white lion, which made him feel even more alone. The white cub stopped his shrieking roar and wandered sadly through the woods.

Meanwhile, in the little town close to the deep pine woods, a boy ran into the general store where everyone always gathered to talk. He was excited.

"Guess what I saw, guess what I saw?" he yelled. Everyone stopped talking.

"What did you see, Jimmy?" they asked.

"I was walking near the woods today and I saw a big white cat."

Everyone was quiet for a moment. Then some of the other boys laughed.

One of the men said, "A big white cat? What you talkin' about, boy? Why, there ain't no such thing as a big white cat. A little white cat maybe, but not a big white cat."

"No sir, no sir," said Jimmy, being as polite as he could be, "it was a big white cat. Big as a young mountain lion, but white."

Now everyone laughed.

"It's true," said Jimmy. "It's true. I saw the big white cat just in the edge of the woods."

Jimmy's mother, who was shopping in the store, shook her head and said, "Jimmy, your imagination gets the best of you sometimes."

"That boy's always been a dreamer," said one of the ladies quietly.

"Kinda peculiar," said another.

Then one of the men said, "Now, who knows? Maybe Jimmy seen some kind of a wampus cat."

"Yes sir, boy," somebody else said. "That's what it is. It's a wampus cat."

"What's a wampus cat?" asked Jimmy.

"Well, he's a very special kind of cat," said a third man, winking at the other two men. "I myself haven't seen one in years around here, but, of course, I bet if you could get a picture of that cat, the *Commercial Appeal* newspaper up in Memphis would pay $10 for it." He grinned at the others as he said it.

"I'll do it," said Jimmy. "I'll borrow mama's old Kodak camera and get a picture of the wampus cat."

Everyone laughed, and only then did Jimmy realize they were joking.

"You don't believe me," he said. "But you will when I get a picture of the cat!"

The next day when Jimmy walked through town, the blacksmith, who was putting shoes on a horse, called to him, "Hey, Jimmy. You seen the wampus cat today?" And the men in the blacksmith shop laughed.

The barber stepped out of his shop and said, "Jimmy, you bring that wampus cat in here and I'll shave all that white hair off him."

"Nobody believes me," thought Jimmy, feeling lonely, "but I'll show them."

So, just as he'd promised, he took his mother's Kodak camera and started out into the woods. Deeper and deeper he went. He saw squirrels and rabbits and a fox, snakes and a deer. He looked up into the tree and saw the wise owl. He even saw the field mouse. But he did not see the white cat. Then he smelled something that scared him. It was smoke!

Jimmy followed the smoke deeper into the woods and found what he had feared: a small grass fire. He tried to stamp out the flames with his feet, but the fire was spreading too fast. He set the camera down, took off his jacket, and tried to beat out the flames. But all he did was catch his jacket on fire. "I better run for town," he thought.

Just as he turned to run, he saw the white cat. He froze in his footsteps. The mountain lion had smelled the smoke and, never having seen fire before, was coming to find out what it was.

"The wampus cat!" cried Jimmy. He remembered the camera but was so scared he could not pick it up.

The young lion was scared too, and he was confused. "Wampus cat?" he said to himself. "I thought I was a mountain lion."

But he did not think about that long because he saw the fire. He was even more afraid of the fire than he was of the boy. Then the boy said, "What am I going to do?"

He began to yell, "Fire, fire, fire!" But his voice was not strong enough to reach town. Other animals saw the fire and they began to call in their own voices, "Fire, fire!" But their voices were not strong enough to reach town. The other mountain lions came.

They saw the fire and began to roar, "Fire, fire!" Their voices were scary but their roars were not loud enough to reach town.

Jimmy said to all the animals, "I'm gonna run to town. I hope I won't be too late."

Just then the white young lion, who never wanted to try to roar because everyone made fun of him, opened his mouth to roar. "Fire, fiiiire!"

His voice was so loud that Jimmy held his ears. It carried through the woods and into the town.

"What was that?" asked the barber.

"I don't know," said the blacksmith, "but it sure sounds like trouble."

"And Jimmy's off in those woods looking for the wampus cat," said Jimmy's mother.

All the people started for the woods. They followed the shriek and in a few minutes came to Jimmy and the wampus cat and the other animals.

"See?" said Jimmy. "I told you he was white."

People stared at the white lion, who was shy because he thought they were going to laugh at him.

"Isn't he beautiful?" said Jimmy's mother. The people all agreed that he was beautiful.

"We don't have time to admire him," said the blacksmith. "We'd better put out that grass fire."

The people stomped on the flames, and some filled their hats with water from the stream. Together, they put out the fire. When the fire was out they looked around for the cat, but he was gone. He was with the other lions heading back to their home, deeper in the woods.

"They said you were beautiful," said one of the lions.

"And your roar saved the woods from burning," said another.

From then on, all the mountain lions wanted to be his friend. And although he was a mountain lion and not anything else, the wise owl had heard the people call him a "wampus cat." So the owl told the animals, "Yes sir, he's a wampus cat. My granddaddy used to tell me about them."

From that time on, he was known as the wampus cat. As for Jimmy, he did not ever get a picture. But the people treated him like a hero and never doubted his word again.

Often Jimmy and the wampus cat would meet where the fire had been. There they would sit under the trees and remember the day that the animals and the people stopped caring about how different they were.

And that is how there came to be the one and only wampus cat in the deep dark pine woods of Mississippi way back in the back-before times.

LESSONS OF THE HEART

In this story, an outcast's gifts help others learn to appreciate and respect their differences. Jimmy's need for respect and his efforts to earn respect help both him and the wampus cat gain a place among their communities. Respect for one another, including our differences, is the foundation of any community.

Story Notes

Jim wrote this tale as a bedtime story for Ben, the son of his good friend Norman Lear. It has the setting and some of the language of Jim's growing up in the deep dark pine woods of northern Mississippi—way back in the back-before times. The wampus cat was a creature from American folklore, in which the character is sometimes a cougar and sometimes a fanciful monster.

YOUR TURN TO TELL A STORY

Everyone has a story to tell, but not everyone has a chance or takes the time to tell it.

This is your chance. So, write your own story or write the story of a friend or relative or just use your imagination and make up a story. But try to make your story about how someone demonstrated a virtue or a characteristic that you admire and want to share with others.

_____

_____

_____

_____

_____

_____

_____

SELECTED BIBLIOGRAPHY

Print Books and E-books

Cowell, Edward B. *The Jātaka or Stories of the Buddha's Former Births.* Cambridge, 1895.

Creeden, Sharon. *Fair Is Fair: World Folktales of Justice.* Little Rock AR: August House Publishers, 1997.

Erdoes, Richard, and Alfonso Ortiz. *American Indian Myths and Legends.* New York: Pantheon Books, 2006.

Foster, Edward E. *Amis and Amiloun, Robert of Cisyle, and Sir Amadace.* Kalamazoo MI: Western Michigan University, Medieval Institute Publications, 2007.

Ginzburg, Natalie. "The Little Virtues." In *The Little Virtues* (1962; repr., New York: Arcade Publishing, 2013). Available online at <https://www.stoa.org.uk/topics/education/Natalia%20Ginzburg%20-%20The%20Little%20Virtues.pdf>.

Grimm, Jacob, Wilhelm Grimm, James Stern, and Josef Scharl. *Grimm's Complete Fairy Tales: The Complete Grimm's Fairy Tales.* New York: Pantheon Books, 1972.

Handford, S. A., and Aesop. *Fables of Aesop.* London UK: Penguin Books, 1988.

Hawthorne, Nathaniel. *A Wonder-Book* and *Tanglewood Tales.* 1851 and 1853. Republished, Wickford RI: North Books, 2002.

Jones, D. P. *Welsh Legends and Fairy Lore.* New York: Barnes & Noble, 1997.

Keding, Dan, and Kathleen A. Brinkmann. *The Gift of the Unicorn and Other Animal Helper Tales for Storytellers, Educators, and Librarians.* Libraries Unlimited, 2016.

Kuss, Danièle, Jean Torton, and Gilles Ragache. *Incas.* Myths & Legends Series. Bath: Cherrytree Books, 1994.

Longfellow, Henry W. *Tales of a Wayside Inn.* Boston: Houghton, Mifflin and Company, 1888.

Masey, Mary L., and Helen Basilevsky. *Stories of the Steppes: Kazakh Folktales.* New York: McKay, 1968.

Morris, William. *The Earthly Paradise.* Hammersmith: Kelmscott Press, 1896.

Perrault, Charles. *Perrault's Complete Fairy Tales.* London: Puffin, 1999.

Powers, Mabel. *Stories the Iroquois Tell Their Children.* New York: American Book Company, 1917.

Reed, Gwendolyn E., and Stella Snead. *The Talkative Beasts: Myths, Fables, and Poems of India.* New York: Lothrop, Lee & Shepard Co, 1969.

Retan, Walter, and Linda Medley. *Favorite Tales from Many Lands.* New York: Grosset & Dunlap, 1989.

Rugoff, Milton A. *The Penguin Book of World Folk Tales.* 1913. Republished, New York: Penguin Books, 1977.

Ryder, Arthur W. *The Panchatantra of Vishnu Sharma.* Chicago: University of Chicago Press, 1925.

Untermeyer, Louis, and Mae Gerhard. *The Firebringer, and Other Great Stories: Fifty-five Legends That Live Forever.* New York: M. Evans (distributed in association with Lippincott, Philadelphia), 1968.

Websites

"Blizzard of 1888." *Nebraska State Historical Society.* January 2001. <http://www.nebraskahistory.org/publish/publicat/timeline/ blizzard_of_1888.htm>.

"Marathon Man Akhwari Demonstrates Superhuman Spirit." *Olympic.org.* <https://www.olympic.org/news/marathon-man-akhwari-demonstrates-superhuman-spirit>.

Potter, Sean. "Retrospect: January 12, 1888: The Children's Blizzard." *Weatherwise.* January-February 2012. <http://www. weatherwise.org/Archives/Back%20Issues/2012/January-February%202012/retrospect-full.html>.

"The Resurrection of Henry 'Box' Brown." *Virginia Historical Society.* <http://www.vahistorical.org/collections-and-resources/ virginia-history-explorer/resurrection-henry-box-brown>.

"The Wampus Cat." Retold by S. E. Schlosser. *American* Folklore. Ghost Stories. <http://americanfolklore.net/folklore/2010/08/ the_wampus_cat.html>.

Story and storytelling websites are legion. One particularly fun site that adds new stories every week is Amy Friedman and Meredith Johnson's *Tell Me a Story.* www.uexpress.com/tell-me-a-story/.

James A. Autry, a former Fortune 500 executive, is an author, poet, and consultant whose work has had a significant influence on leadership thinking. He is the author of thirteen books, and his writings have appeared in many anthologies and magazines. Autry received considerable national attention when he was one of the poets featured in Bill Moyers' special 1989 series, *The Power of the Word*, on PBS, and in Moyers' 1995 book, *The Language of Life*. In 2012 Autry appeared on *Moyers & Company* on PBS, and his work has been featured on Garrison Keillor's *Writer's Almanac* on National Public Radio. Autry serves on the national advisory board of Poets & Writers, Inc., and was a founder of the Des Moines National Poetry Festival. He holds four honorary degrees and is the recipient of a lifetime achievement award for service to the humanities from the Iowa Humanities Board. Autry lives in Des Moines, Iowa, with his wife, former lieutenant governor of Iowa Sally Pederson, and their thirty-four-year-old son. He has two sons by a previous marriage and is a grandfather of two.

Rick Autry has been a lawyer working for the state of Iowa for more than thirty years. For seventeen years he was an Iowa assistant attorney general representing the Iowa Civil Rights Commission. He is a frequent speaker on employment law at legal seminars and author of *Word Origins for Lawyers*, published by the American Bar Association. He and his wife, Lyn, have been married for thirty-five years. Their two sons have graduated college and are both pursuing post-graduate education.

CPSIA information can be obtained
at www.ICGtesting.com
Printed in the USA
LVOW10s0041080118
562195LV00009B/176/P